BLOCKBUSTERS QUIZ BOOK 2

This book adaptation of *Blockbusters*, the very successful Central television series game, can be used in one of two ways. By yourself you can solve the clues as you would a crossword puzzle, writing the answers in the spaces provided and shading or colouring in the hexagons; or, you can play it as a game with friends, one being the quizmaster and two being competitors, one trying to get a linking pattern of hexagons across and one down.

Whether you solve the clues yourself, or with friends, you'll have hours of amusement and have masses of information at your fingertips.

Also in the Blockbusters series in Sphere Books:

BLOCKBUSTERS QUIZ BOOK 1
BLOCKBUSTERS QUIZ BOOK 3
BLOCKBUSTERS QUIZ BOOK 4
BLOCKBUSTERS GOLD RUN

Blockbusters
Quiz Book 2

**Based on the Central Independent Television series
produced in association with Mark Goodson and
Talbot Television Ltd**

SPHERE BOOKS LIMITED

First published in Great Britain
by Sphere Books Ltd 1985
27 Wrights Lane, London W8 5TZ
Copyright © 1985 by Sphere Books Ltd
Central logo copyright © 1982
Central Independent Television plc.
Central Television programmes © 1983, 1984, 1985
Central Independent Television plc.
Reprinted 1985 (five times), 1986 (five times), 1987

TRADE
MARK

Set in Times

Printed and bound in Great Britain by
Cox & Wyman Ltd, Reading

Blockbusters
Quiz Book 2

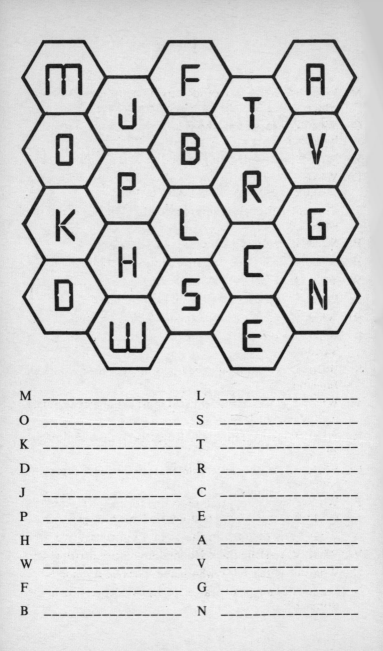

M _____   L _____

O _____   S _____

K _____   T _____

D _____   R _____

J _____   C _____

P _____   E _____

H _____   A _____

W _____   V _____

F _____   G _____

B _____   N _____

M: What 'M' is the way of identifying a street in America, which would be called a 'High Street' here?

O: What 'O' is a person who is larger than usual, and needs big clothes?

K: What 'K' is the Hindu god of Fire and Light?

D: What 'D' received a proposal of marriage, without a carriage, but with a bike made for two?

J: What 'J' in the calendar is named after the Mother of the gods?

P: What 'P' is sixteen ounces?

H: What 'H' is pickled and made into a roll mop?

W: What 'W' wrote 'Ain't Misbehavin'' and was called Fats?

F: What 'F' is a ball wrongly served at tennis?

B: What 'B' stars Endora, Samantha, and Darrin?

L: What 'L' gives psychiatric advice for a small fee in 'Peanuts'?

S: What 'S' is a hunting expedition in Africa, or a park in England?

T: What 'T' is the instrument said to waken the dead at last on Judgement Day?

R: What 'R' is a keeper in a Royal park or a senior girl guide?

C: What 'C' is the vegetable that is used to represent coolness?

E: What 'E' was a royal who was one for the girls, came to the throne late in life, and married Alexandra?

A: What 'A' is the man in charge of a monastery?

V: What 'V' was Sherlock Holmes' favourite instrument?

G: What 'G' is the Eddy who made 'Electric Avenue'?

N: What 'N' is a type of orange, or a small depression in the stomach?

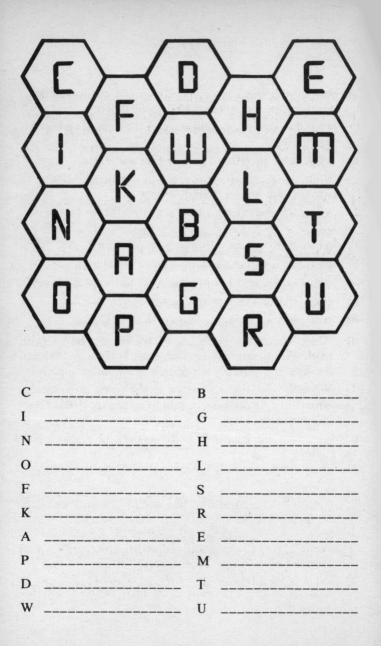

C _____ B _____

I _____ G _____

N _____ H _____

O _____ L _____

F _____ S _____

K _____ R _____

A _____ E _____

P _____ M _____

D _____ T _____

W _____ U _____

C: What 'C' is a flexible string of connected metal links?

I: What 'I' means to press, or wedge, as in the case of wisdom teeth that are too close?

N: What 'N' was the title taken by Mr Morris of Morris Motors?

O: What 'O' goes before time, coat and cast?

F: What 'F' is the popular name for a blue flower called Myosotts?

K: What 'K' is what you do on a door?

A: What 'A' is the name given to a bumptious, conceited, know-all who thinks he's smart?

P: What 'P' was the country invaded by Hitler in 1939?

D: What 'D' were the *R.100* and the *Hindenburg*?

W: What 'W' comes before cream, up and away?

B: What 'B' was the surname of the singer, Harry, who made the hit records, 'Banana Boat Song' and 'Island in the Sun'?

G: What 'G' is an illness known as the rich man's curse?

H: What 'H' is north of Nicaragua?

L: What 'L' was Jimmy Osmond's lover from Liverpool?

S: What 'S' goes before pancake, egg and broth?

R: What 'R' is a colloquial term for a newspaper, usually the local one?

E: What 'E' is a riddle, puzzling thing, or something difficult to understand?

M: What 'M' had a brother who worshipped a golden calf?

T: What 'T' is the saint associated with the teaching hospital founded by Florence Nightingale?

U: What 'U' is a bike used in circuses, with only one wheel?

G _____   C _____

Y _____   L _____

A _____   P _____

T _____   O _____

W _____   H _____

S _____   F _____

U _____   D _____

B _____   M _____

E _____   J _____

N _____   R _____

G: What 'G' is the principal city in the Clyde?

Y: What 'Y' is a sailing boat?

A: What 'A' is the four weeks that commemorate the first and second coming of Christ?

T: What 'T' is the Michael Jackson album that includes 'Billy Jean' and 'Beat It'?

W: What 'W' is the tree up which the mistaken bark?

S: What 'S' is the dog that tries to shoot down the Red Baron?

U: What 'U' is the mass of plants, shrubs and bushes, beneath the trees of a wood?

B: What 'B' can be conical, can, spherical or mooring?

E: What 'E' goes before ball, bath and glass?

N: What 'N' is the point of a quill, or fountain pen?

C: What 'C' is the occupation of Karl Heinz Stockhausen?

L: What 'L' gave up the name Ulyanov and founded the Bolshevik Party?

P: What 'P' is the Jane Austen novel about the secret engagement of Anne Elliott?

O: What 'O' is the most used lubricant?

H: What 'H' do you feel when you want something to eat?

F: What 'F' are studied by a biologist called an ichthyologist?

D: What 'D' is ten cents in US money?

M: What 'M' is the paranoid android in the 'Hitch Hiker's Guide to the Galaxy'?

J: What 'J' is a stream of water ejected from a nozzle or spout?

R: What 'R' is someone who deals in stolen goods; but also means the earpiece of a telephone?

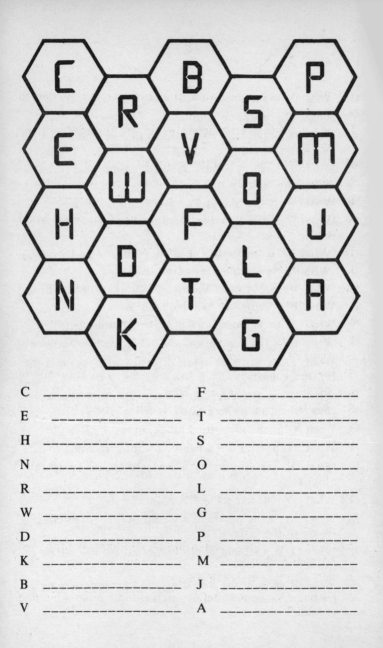

C _____ F _____

E _____ T _____

H _____ S _____

N _____ O _____

R _____ L _____

W _____ G _____

D _____ P _____

K _____ M _____

B _____ J _____

V _____ A _____

C: What 'C' is a type of sofa, or an earl who wrote letters to his son?

E: What 'E' in the academic world are presided over by invigilators?

H: What 'H' was one of the seven dwarfs?

N: What 'N' means any bovine animal, and also 'Tidy'?

R: What 'R' were trained by Cecil Boyd Rochfort?

W: What 'W' is the popular name of the little white wood anemone?

D: What 'D' is the patron saint of Wales?

K: What 'K' is a school for young children?

B: What 'B' is the South American Republic in which Zuazo became president in 1982?

V: What 'V' is a saint whose feast day is 14th February?

F: What 'F' is the first name by which Mr Knox is known in 'Some Experiences of an Irish RM'?

T: What 'T' are carried in the jawbone, and are made of dentine?

S: What 'S' is a speech in a play which is spoken by an actor to himself?

O: What 'O' is a fruit, grown in Spain and Italy, that is sold green and black and produces oil?

L: What 'L' comes before turn, wing and over?

G: What 'G' is any light filmy substance but especially the webs of small spiders?

P: What 'P' is the colourful part of a flower?

M: What 'M' were Adrian Boult, William Walton and Arthur Rubinstein?

J: What 'J' is a make of orange?

A: What 'A' comes before suggestion, biography and mobile?

F _____   N _____

O _____   J _____

I _____   S _____

R _____   H _____

T _____   V _____

A _____   G _____

E _____   M _____

B _____   W _____

P _____   C _____

D _____   L _____

F: What 'F' is a lucky accidental stroke?

O: What 'O' is an unreasonably persistent idea or interest?

I: What 'I' obstructs or hinders?

R: What 'R' is the sport indulged in by members of a club called Leander?

T: What 'T' is the bridge in Scotland that is among the ten longest in the world?

A: What 'A' is the English name for the sign of the zodiac called Sagittarius?

E: What 'E' played Che Guevara and is an English county?

B: What 'B' is part of a theatre and something you do with your fists?

P: What 'P' is a more genteel word for sweat?

D: What 'D' goes with Stockton, in 1825, in railway history?

N: What 'N' is where 'Operation Overlord' took place?

J: What 'J' is a group of twelve men and women sitting in a court of law?

S: What 'S' is a mixed drink served in a long glass, or what you put a broken arm into?

H: What 'H' pounces, petty, singles and sails, and is flown at game?

V: What 'V' means empty and often goes with null?

G: What 'G' is a rock that has been in British hands since 1704?

M: What 'M' is brown, thick, sticky and syrupy?

W: What 'W' is supposed to be in league with the devil, has a black cat and rides on a broomstick?

C: What 'C' makes a bang in a toy pistol, or when tapped with a hammer?

L: What 'L' is the loch with bonny bonny banks?

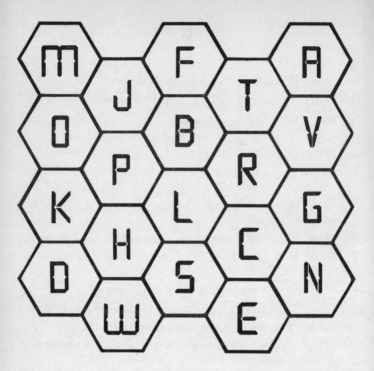

M _____
O _____
K _____
D _____
J _____
P _____
H _____
W _____
F _____
B _____

L _____
S _____
T _____
R _____
C _____
E _____
A _____
V _____
G _____
N _____

M: What 'M' is the familiar first name of the man who celebrated his 100th birthday in the House of Lords?

O: What 'O' is the area furthest from the wicket on a cricket pitch?

K: What 'K' was a Pulitzer Prize winning president of the USA?

D: What 'D' was supplanted by Robespierre, and guillotined in 1794?

J: What 'J' have you got when you are in a flustered state, caused by fright?

P: What 'P' is a game which uses the terms backhander, hooking and chukka?

H: What 'H' is milk that has been treated to stop the cream rising?

W: What 'W' did Daedalus use to fix wings to himself and his son?

F: What 'F' is the barb of an anchor, a whale's tail, or a happy   accident?

B: What 'B' has an airport called Templehof?

L: What 'L' was called Martin and proposed ninety-five theses, for the reform of the Catholic Church?

S: What 'S' means a 'day of rest' and is used by the Jews for Saturday?

T: What 'T' is said to have been the home of Diogenes, probably to show his contempt for riches?

R: What 'R' is a word for 'stale' that is chiefly applied to butter?

C: What 'C' is the sort of love that is only shown in the hope of getting something in reward?

E: What 'E' is the subject in which a book by Adam Smith is a foundation study?

A: What 'A' is the city normally associated with the black, hornless cattle from Angus?

V: What 'V' is famous for its Vaporetti and Lido?

G: What 'G' is the name of the warbler known as the reeler or reel bird?

N: What 'N' is the only word that goes with fangled?

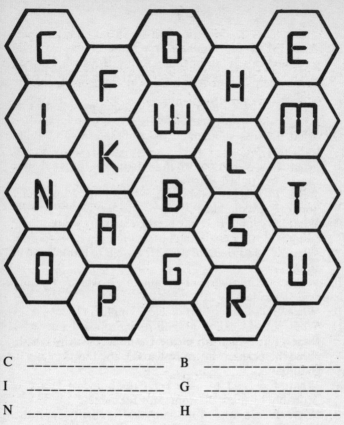

C _____   B _____

I _____   G _____

N _____   H _____

O _____   L _____

F _____   S _____

K _____   R _____

A _____   E _____

P _____   M _____

D _____   T _____

W _____   U _____

C: What 'C' is a brilliant, British, black bowler from Middlesex?

I: What 'I' is a non-metallic element that produces purple vapour and is never found in nature, uncombined?

N: What 'N' are now frequently tabloids?

O: What 'O', who sometimes gets spelt with an H, was the stable boy at the inn?

F: What 'F' are called Dutch or Cambridgeshire Nightingales because of the din they make at night?

K: What 'K' is to carry off by force for ransom?

A: What 'A' is the first name of Mr Cooper who sang, 'School's Out'?

P: What 'P' is the European country that produces most of the world's cork?

D: What 'D' is a warrigal, or Australian wild dog?

W: What 'W' is the name given to the French-speaking people of Southern Belgium?

B: What 'B' is the capital of Yugoslavia?

G: What 'G' is a Scottish castle connected with Macbeth, where the Queen Mother spent her childhood?

H: What 'H' means salubrious?

L: What 'L' is the part of your ear where you wear an earring?

S: What 'S' comes after cinema, television and rood?

R: What 'R' is a name for countless dogs and means 'King' in Latin?

E: What 'E' means 'to go beyond', especially a speed limit?

M: What 'M' is the religious community that is headed by an Imam?

T: What 'T' is a controversial modern armament, or the spear carried by Britannia?

U: What 'U' is a word used for 'relax' which means to undo a coil, or remove from a bobbin?

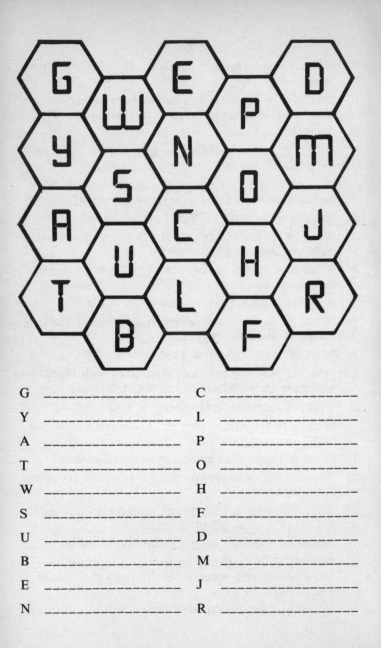

G _____ C _____

Y _____ L _____

A _____ P _____

T _____ O _____

W _____ H _____

S _____ F _____

U _____ D _____

B _____ M _____

E _____ J _____

N _____ R _____

G: What 'G' was Conservative Party Chairman at the time of their 1984 conference?

Y: What 'Y' makes bread rise?

A: What 'A' is a spell, or magic formula, used at the beginning of some conjurers' tricks?

T: What 'T' are coastal birds that can be sooty, arctic or fairy?

W: What 'W' do you cry when you give false alarms?

S: What 'S' is a North Yorkshire resort whose fair, Simon and Garfunkel sing about?

U: What 'U' means omnipresence?

B: What 'B' is a type of shoe, or an Irish accent?

E: What 'E' sounds like tiring, but means thorough or comprehensive?

N: What 'N' was the statesman whose daughter became Prime Minister of India?

C: What 'C' is the patron saint of travellers?

L: What 'L' is the name or title given to the first violin in a symphony orchestra?

P: What 'P' was an early form of gramophone, using cylinders not discs?

O: What 'O' is a vegetable, also used to make a yellow dye?

H: What 'H' is a large building for housing aircraft?

F: What 'F' was named after Mr Douglas and is covered with needles?

D: What 'D' was the name given to any extinct reptiles like the Iguanodon and Brontosaurus?

M: What 'M' is traditionally regarded as the author of the second gospel?

J: What 'J' is to cast someone off after you've promised to marry them?

R: What 'R' is a musical performance given by one person?

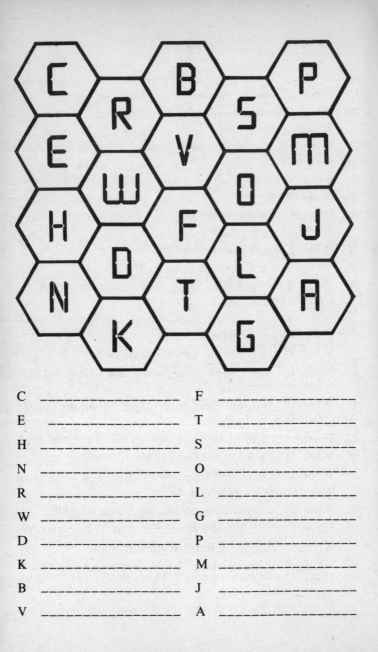

C _____   F _____

E _____   T _____

H _____   S _____

N _____   O _____

R _____   L _____

W _____   G _____

D _____   P _____

K _____   M _____

B _____   J _____

V _____   A _____

C: What 'C' means to go round to drum up votes?

E: What 'E' are directed downwards at the start of a game of Bingo?

H: What 'H' has kinds called poplar, privit and death's head?

N: What 'N' threw Shadrach, Meshach and Abednego into the fiery furnace?

R: What 'R' is a fast current, like the water channelled into a mill?

W: What 'W' causes rill erosion, gully erosion and sheet erosion?

D: What 'D' is a metal rod that shows when a car engine needs oil?

K: What 'K' contains a public telephone?

B: What 'B' is the important German city divided into East and West by a wall?

V: What 'V' is a large bird of prey?

F: What 'F' are surgical pincers?

T: What 'T' was the nation that produced the Seljuk Dynasty?

S: What 'S' is a short gaiter, or the spawn of a shellfish?

O: What 'O' is a theatrical Lord called Laurence?

L: What 'L' is cloth made from flax fibres?

G: What 'G' are carried by a caddy?

P: What 'P' comes before hanger, chase and weight?

M: What 'M' is an island whose chief town is Tobermory?

J: What 'J' is the Mick in the Rolling Stones?

A: What 'A' is the limb of the sea between Greece and Turkey?

F   —————————————

O   —————————————

I   —————————————

R   —————————————

T   —————————————

A   —————————————

E   —————————————

B   —————————————

P   —————————————

D   —————————————

N   —————————————

J   —————————————

S   —————————————

H   —————————————

V   —————————————

G   —————————————

M   —————————————

W   —————————————

C   —————————————

L   —————————————

F: What 'F' is a disastrous shortage of food?

O: What 'O' is the opposite of on?

I: What 'I' is a very small child?

R: What 'R' is carried by a viaduct?

T: What 'T' is a sikh's headgear?

A: What 'A' was known as the 'Scourge of God' and was leader of the Huns?

E: What 'E' was the descriptive name given to royalists and others who fled the French revolution?

B: What 'B' comes before beard, stocking and whale?

P: What 'P' is any large, thick skinned animal, like a rhino or an elephant?

D: What 'D' is the word used to describe the decorative arrangement of goods in a shop window?

N: What 'N' is the society that collects money for the Provisional IRA in America?

J: What 'J' does one have to keep up with?

S: What 'S' is one more than sixteen?

H: What 'H' is a woman's riding dress, religious clothes or a settled tendency?

V: What 'V' is a fear of heights?

G: What 'G' is an abbreviation of Luigi and sounds like a child's word for horse?

M: What 'M' are proverbially made into mountains?

W: What 'W' is armed conflict and have been called Boer, First and Second?

C: What 'C' are cowboys' leather trousers without a seat?

L: What 'L' is a visible form of electro-magnetic radiation?

M _____ L _____

O _____ S _____

K _____ T _____

D _____ R _____

J _____ C _____

P _____ E _____

H _____ A _____

W _____ V _____

F _____ G _____

B _____ N _____

M: What 'M' is the opposite of minimum?

O: What 'O' is one of the competing teams in the University Boat Race?

K: What 'K' was an African political figure called Jomo?

D: What 'D' is the principal river at Ulm?

J: What 'J' is a rider of race horses?

P: What 'P' means many coloured?

H: What 'H' is said to exist among thieves?

W: What 'W' is the surface to which stucco is applied?

F: What 'F' is a kind of sword, metal-coated paper or a frustrate?

B: What 'B' is the national field game of the USA?

L: What 'L' precedes anaesthetic and time?

S: What 'S' is the fish which is the source of caviar?

T: What 'T' is the day of the week that follows Monday?

R: What 'R' is the name given to the fifty-eight people who signed the death warrant of Charles I?

C: What 'C' was British Prime Minister in 1978?

E: What 'E' decides what goes in a newspaper?

A: What 'A' were Ralph Richardson, David Niven and Richard Burton?

V: What 'V' is a female fox?

G: What 'G' is the American squirrel introduced to Britain in the 19th century?

N: What 'N' consists of seven cervical vertebrae?

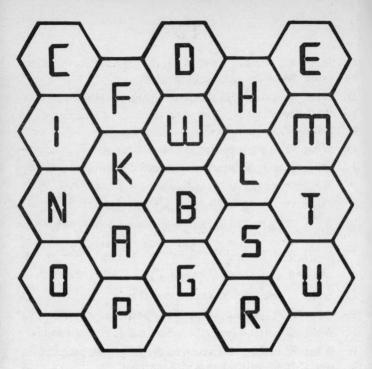

C _____
I _____
N _____
O _____
F _____
K _____
A _____
P _____
D _____
W _____

B _____
G _____
H _____
L _____
S _____
R _____
E _____
M _____
T _____
U _____

C: What 'C' is often used to extend or adulterate coffee, especially in France?

I: What 'I' is the wind that blows nobody good?

N: What 'N' is called Sidney and is one of Australia's most distinguished painters?

O: What 'O' is the most important fishing port of Belgium?

F: What 'F' is the sweetest of the simple sugars and is found in honey and fruit?

K: What 'K' is used as an expletive, but means ladies underwear?

A: What 'A' is the solution of a base in water?

P: What 'P' is the industry with unions called Natsopa and Sogat?

D: What 'D' is the name of the first, or tonic, note in the Solfa or solfeggio system?

W: What 'W' is the most northerly of the Pacific States of America?

B: What 'B' can be mouse-eared or pipistrelle?

G: What 'G' is exemplified by 'For what we are about to receive may the Lord make us truly thankful'?

H: What 'H' makes water, when combined with oxygen?

L: What 'L' do you gird up when you prepare for action?

S: What 'S' goes before cloud, warning and porch?

R: What 'R' is completely to destroy something down to ground level, often a building?

E: What 'E' is to root out, or pull up by the roots?

M: What 'M' formed the indigenous population of New Zealand?

T: What 'T' is a projecting tooth seen in elephants, walruses, and wild boar?

U: What 'U' is incompletely cooked – like the best roast beef?

G _____   C _____

Y _____   L _____

A _____   P _____

T _____   O _____

W _____   H _____

S _____   F _____

U _____   D _____

B _____   M _____

E _____   J _____

N _____   R _____

13

G: What 'G' was killed in a fairy story, by Jack?

Y: What 'Y' is made from fermented milk?

A: What 'A' is Britain's only poisonous snake?

T: What 'T' is the little wiggly bit by which a vine climbs and clings?

W: What 'W' is a cereal called triticum vulgare?

S: What 'S' is a pedigree stallion when he's a father?

U: What 'U' means vacant, empty or idle?

B: What 'B' are marks of parenthesis in punctuation?

E: What 'E' was once ruled by a son of King Solomon, and is the country whose capital is called Addis Ababa?

N: What 'N' was the official language of Oceania, which was designed to diminish the range of thought in the book '1984'?

C: What 'C' is the common constituent of soot, coal and diamonds?

L: What 'L' comes before mark, lord and lubber?

P: What 'P' is either a blue-flowered trailing plant, or an old fashioned name for a shellfish you eat off a pin?

O: What 'O' is the abbreviation of Oxfordshire?

H: What 'H' strangled serpents in babyhood, and did tests of strength most of his life?

F: What 'F' is the nautical, legal and archaic word for the morning?

D: What 'D' is the site of the fast breeder-reactor power station in Caithness?

M: What 'M' is a tree with winged seeds that produces sugary syrup?

J: What 'J' described himself as 'a writer of dictionaries a harmless drudge'?

R: What 'R' is the carpet rolled out for dignitaries?

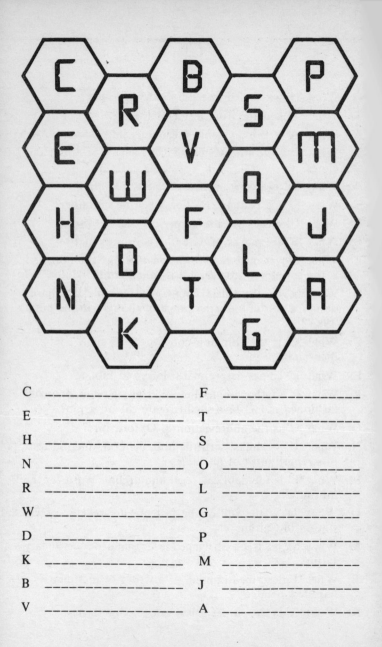

C _____   F _____

E _____   T _____

H _____   S _____

N _____   O _____

R _____   L _____

W _____   G _____

D _____   P _____

K _____   M _____

B _____   J _____

V _____   A _____

C: What 'C' is the city at the mouth of the Taff?

E: What 'E' is an organic catalyst?

H: What 'H' invented Melstock in Wessex?

N: What 'N' was the fifth Roman Emperor and a very nasty bit of work?

R: What 'R' is the companion of Doctor Who, called K9?

W: What 'W' is the chief agricultural product of Paarl in South Africa?

D: What 'D' is a pile of snow made by the wind?

K: What 'K' is a bell rung at a person's funeral?

B: What 'B' made a plan that became the Health Service?

V: What 'V' was a famous 17th century painter?

F: What 'F' contains your tarsals and metatarsals?

T: What 'T' is the name of the process by which hides are turned into leather?

S: What 'S' is a Japanese drink made from rice?

O: What 'O' is Cleopatra's Needle?

L: What 'L' is a device for measuring a ship's speed or distance covered?

G: What 'G' was the fleece sought by Jason?

P: What 'P' was a Jew from Tarsus, originally called Saul?

M: What 'M' is called Iris, and wrote 'A Severed Head'?

J: What 'J' is black, a type of aeroplane and a fast stream of water?

A: What 'A' is the German word for a motorway?

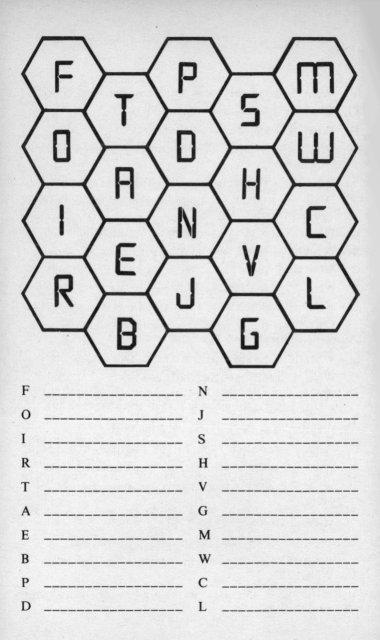

F _____   N _____

O _____   J _____

I _____   S _____

R _____   H _____

T _____   V _____

A _____   G _____

E _____   M _____

B _____   W _____

P _____   C _____

D _____   L _____

F: What 'F' is the thing the Americans call 'Old Glory'?

O: What 'O' is where astronomers work?

I: What 'I' is a medicine administered via a syringe?

R: What 'R' is made into gloves to protect your hands, and into bicycle tyres?

T: What 'T' is the site of a rattlesnake's rattle?

A: What 'A' was the eldest daughter of Sir Robert Laurie?

E: What 'E' was the second Prime Minister of the present Queen's reign?

B: What 'B' was a Frenchman who crossed Niagara on a tightrope?

P: What 'P' is a universal remedy?

D: What 'D' is associated with Grand Coulee, Kariba and Aswan?

N: What 'N' was the description of the idealised savage, or primitive man, of romantic literature?

J: What 'J' is a stick that gives off a perfume when burned?

S: What 'S' is a fish that returns to its birthplace to spawn, and has given its name to one of the shades of pink?

H: What 'H' has a capital called Budapest?

V: What 'V' is a wanderer or vagrant and is considered a rascal?

G: What 'G' is the name of a painter that's been given to the ESA mission to explore Halley's comet?

M: What 'M' is the economic policy beloved by Geoffrey Howe and Mrs Thatcher?

W: What 'W' is an old-fashioned term for radio?

C: What 'C' is Lutyens' monument for the fallen in Whitehall?

L: What 'L' is the part of the fig-tree associated with modesty?

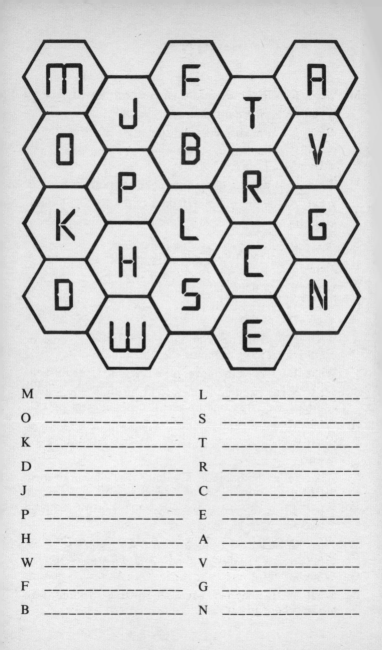

M _____ L _____

O _____ S _____

K _____ T _____

D _____ R _____

J _____ C _____

P _____ E _____

H _____ A _____

W _____ V _____

F _____ G _____

B _____ N _____

M: What 'M' was the mountain first successfully climbed by Edward Whymper?

O: What 'O' is the surname of Alan, Wayne, Merrill, Jay and Donny?

K: What 'K' is to deprive of life?

D: What 'D' is the MP called Tam, who started the agitation over the *Belgrano* affair?

J: What 'J' is called 'the golden, with milk and honey blessed'?

P: What 'P' is what Australians call British immigrants?

H: What 'H' is a man with a domineering wife said to be?

W: What 'W' said poetry had its origins in 'emotion recollected in tranquillity'?

F: What 'F' is what happens to the dovecots as a result of a domestic scandal?

B: What 'B' is an instrument for blowing up a fire or a forge?

L: What 'L' was Dorothy Stanton's stage-name in her many movies with Hope and Crosby?

S: What 'S' is a non-fattening sweetener?

T: What 'T' was a city plunged into a long war by the abduction of Helen?

R: What 'R' means quick?

C: What 'C' comes before up, word and fire?

E: What 'E' is the first name of the owner of a yacht called 'Morning Cloud'?

A: What 'A' used to be of the white, of the red, or of the blue?

V: What 'V' is a parchment made of lamb, or calf-skin?

G: What 'G' has a president called Karamanlis?

N: What 'N' was the pen name of Mrs Edith Bland, who wrote 'The Railway Children'?

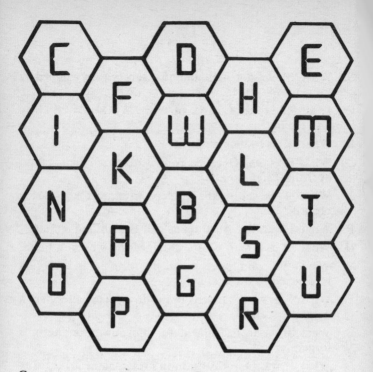

C _____
I _____
N _____
O _____
F _____
K _____
A _____
P _____
D _____
W _____

B _____
G _____
H _____
L _____
S _____
R _____
E _____
M _____
T _____
U _____

C: What 'C' comes before stick, wick and light?

I: What 'I' is to plunge a person below the surface of water as in some forms of baptism?

N: What 'N' is an East Anglican town where the Jockey Club has its HQ?

O: What 'O' is the opposite of pessimism?

F: What 'F' is a picture at the beginning of a book?

K: What 'K' are small decorative objects and bits and pieces of all kinds?

A: What 'A' were sent out by Jesus to preach the Gospels?

P: What 'P' is nightwear that comes in two pieces?

D: What 'D' were Boatswain, Diamond and Rufus, who belonged to Byron, Newton and Churchill?

W: What 'W' is the slender rod carried by fairies and magicians?

B: What 'B' is an army officer's soldier servant?

G: What 'G' is the unit of currency in the Netherlands?

H: What 'H' is the pen name of the vet who wrote, 'Vet in Harness'?

L: What 'L' is another word for an attic?

S: What 'S' precedes ladder, pink and trout?

R: What 'R' was the building in Berlin that burnt down in February 1933?

E: What 'E' is the name of the English Actors' trade union?

M: What 'M' took over 'Family Fortunes' from Bob Monkhouse?

T: What 'T' designed many of Russia's most famous aircraft, including the first supersonic passenger plane?

U: What 'U' is the type of suffrage where everyone can vote?

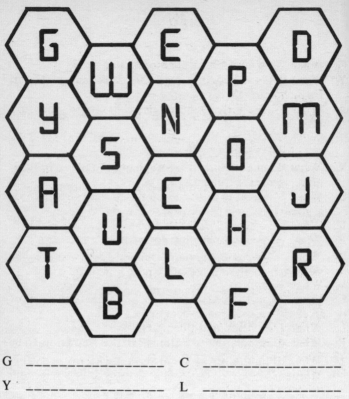

G _____ C _____

Y _____ L _____

A _____ P _____

T _____ O _____

W _____ H _____

S _____ F _____

U _____ D _____

B _____ M _____

E _____ J _____

N _____ R _____

G: What 'G' is a spook or phantom?

Y: What 'Y' is a pudding eaten with milk and is also an English county?

A: What 'A' is a little creature symbolic of hard work and thrift?

T: What 'T' was the best known film character played by Johnny Weismuller?

W: What 'W' likes trees and telegraph poles, and can be pied, great spotted, or green?

S: What 'S' is a lump of wood supporting a railway track, or a gold circle in a pierced ear?

U: What 'U' is the 'U' of USSR?

B: What 'B' comes before words and legs?

E: What 'E' was the zone to keep out the Argentinians during the Falklands episode?

N: What 'N' is forty winks?

C: What 'C' is the public building in which you're most likely to see a hammer-beam roof?

L: What 'L' is black or golden, and fetches game?

P: What 'P' is swearing to a statement that you know to be false?

O: What 'O' are words like cock-a-doodle-doo, hiss and quack-quack?

H: What 'H' is the venue for the Royal Regatta on the Thames?

F: What 'F' is a word for very fair hair, because it is as pale as bleached linen?

D: What 'D' was a German called Rudolf who invented a compression ignition engine?

M: What 'M' is a Portuguese island in the Atlantic and fortified wine?

J: What 'J' is the English equivalent of the Russian name Ivan, and the Welsh name Evan, and the Irish name Shaun?

R: What 'R' is a fibre used for making hats, baskets and mats, and is used for tying up plants?

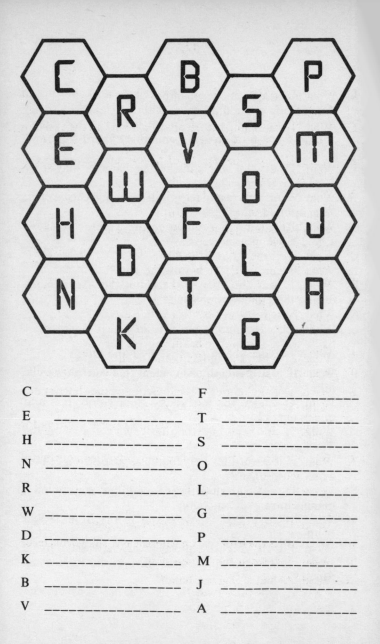

C	_____	F	_____
E	_____	T	_____
H	_____	S	_____
N	_____	O	_____
R	_____	L	_____
W	_____	G	_____
D	_____	P	_____
K	_____	M	_____
B	_____	J	_____
V	_____	A	_____

C: What 'C' is the cry of the crow and the rook, but not of the raven?

E: What 'E' can come before or after 'Yours' at the end of a friendly letter?

H: What 'H' is the preserving of health, often by means of cleanliness?

N: What 'N' can be lace, tie or cloth?

R: What 'R' was the lover of Juliet?

W: What 'W' is England's oldest public school?

D: What 'D' is a dog called Dinmont or a man who pays attention to his dress?

K: What 'K' is a famous make of camera?

B: What 'B' is the hero of a strip cartoon and whose other name is Bruce Wayne?

V: What 'V' is a variety entertainment?

F: What 'F' comes before song, dance and lore?

T: What 'T' is a ship designed to carry liquid cargo in bulk?

S: What 'S' is the name for the longest and the shortest day of the year when the sun appears to stand still?

O: What 'O' goes with sage, in the traditional stuffing for duck?

L: What 'L' was Robert Dudley, much fancied courtier of Queen Elizabeth I?

G: What 'G' is still sometimes tested for quality on a touchstone?

P: What 'P' goes before fruit, flower and play?

M: What 'M' is the fruit tree on whose leaves silkworms feed?

J: What 'J' is worn for horse-riding?

A: What 'A' had a ragtime band?

F _____   N _____

O _____   J _____

I _____   S _____

R _____   H _____

T _____   V _____

A _____   G _____

E _____   M _____

B _____   W _____

P _____   C _____

D _____   L _____

F: What 'F' are cultivated by pisciculture?

O: What 'O' is a prize presented to actors and directors?

I: What 'I' is a severe examination by questioning?

R: What 'R' is a valley in Mid-Glamorgan in South Wales, famous for coal-mining?

T: What 'T' comes after reflecting, refracting or Schmidt?

A: What 'A' is the name usually given to the King James version of The Bible?

E: What 'E' comes after red, white and blue in maritime situations?

B: What 'B' is the type of saw used for logs and often referred to as Swedish?

P: What 'P' is a support for a temporary bridge across a river?

D: What 'D' is a wooden duck or pigeon?

N: What 'N' are the tricks you can't teach an old dog?

J: What 'J' was a wren's first name?

S: What 'S' are demonstrated by the statements 'you have hissed all mystery lessons', and 'taken the town drain'?

H: What 'H' is an ancient children's game based on the idea of not treading on lines?

V: What 'V' is someone who can throw his voice without moving his lips?

G: What 'G' is a topographical (or geographical) index?

M: What 'M' are you said to get for old rope, if something comes easily?

W: What 'W' is interwoven twigs and used to be used in building with daub?

C: What 'C' is a period of a hundred years?

L: What 'L' are you told to use when you are being stupid?

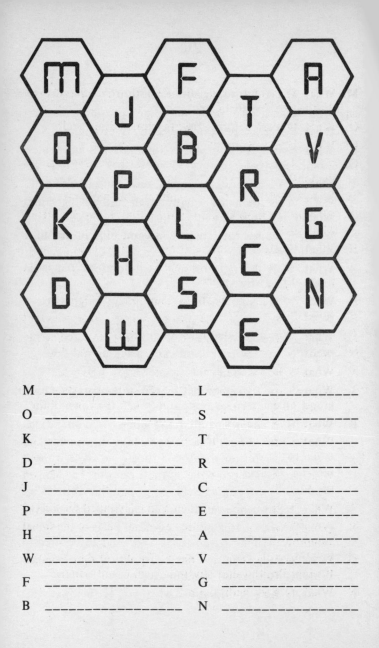

M _____   L _____

O _____   S _____

K _____   T _____

D _____   R _____

J _____   C _____

P _____   E _____

H _____   A _____

W _____   V _____

F _____   G _____

B _____   N _____

M: What 'M' is the saint to which a London church said to be 'In the fields' is dedicated?

O: What 'O' goes before glory, fashioned and maid?

K: What 'K' is a baby cat?

D: What 'D' are the curved uprights that carry a ship's lifeboat?

J: What 'J' is known to its inhabitants as Nippon?

P: What 'P' was an Egyptian ruling dynasty that came from Macedonia?

H: What 'H' is a stew nominally associated with Lancashire?

W: What 'W' is the merry-thought or breast bone of a roast bird?

F: What 'F' is a note played or sung below true pitch?

B: What 'B' is a lawyer raised to when he becomes a Judge?

L: What 'L' is made in the form of bobbin, pillow and needle point?

S: What 'S' is a secret agent?

T: What 'T' is a jewelled head-dress worn by women on grand occasions?

R: What 'R' is demanded after kidnap?

C: What 'C' do you strike when you take down tents and move off?

E: What 'E' was the pen-name of the author of 'The Mill on the Floss'?

A: What 'A' is the sea, of which Venice is called the queen?

V: What 'V' are the thirty-three essential parts of the spinal column?

G: What 'G' is a state that has had political figures called Bishop, Braithwaite, Hudson-Austin, and Scoon?

N: What 'N' goes with pamby?

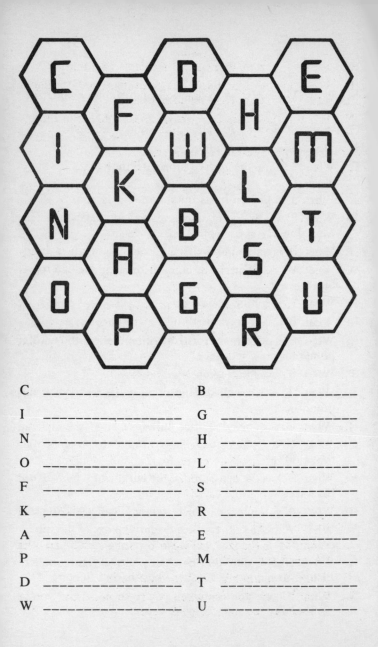

C _____ B _____

I _____ G _____

N _____ H _____

O _____ L _____

F _____ S _____

K _____ R _____

A _____ E _____

P _____ M _____

D _____ T _____

W _____ U _____

C: What 'C' can be alimentary, Regent's or Panama?

I: What 'I' is an island republic, south-east of Greenland, and 500 miles north-west of Scotland?

N: What 'N' is a Canadian province, or a breed of dog?

O: What 'O' was the ancient Greek king whose name is given to a neurotic relationship with the parent?

F: What 'F' comes before dog, lighter and alarm?

K: What 'K' is an Australian marsupial related to the wallaby?

A: What 'A' is a famous 20th century poet with the first names Wystan Hugh?

P: What 'P' is the smallest and least valuable piece in chess?

D: What 'D' means 'become wider or larger', and is often applied to the pupil of the eye?

W: What 'W' is a little tool for beating eggs or cream to a froth?

B: What 'B' had been on a bread-fruit collection expedition when his crew mutinied?

G: What 'G' was one of the seven dwarfs?

H: What 'H' is tiny, sips nectar on the wing, and lives in hot countries?

L: What 'L' is the river that flows through the château country of France?

S: What 'S' goes before plate, fir tree and lining?

R: What 'R' wrote a history of the world while imprisoned in the tower in the early 17th century?

E: What 'E' is a phone number that is deliberately left out of the book?

M: What 'M' is the lace veil worn by Spanish women over the head and shoulders?

T: What 'T' is another word for lukewarm?

U: What 'U' are you on, when you're so poor that you've worn away the soles of your shoes?

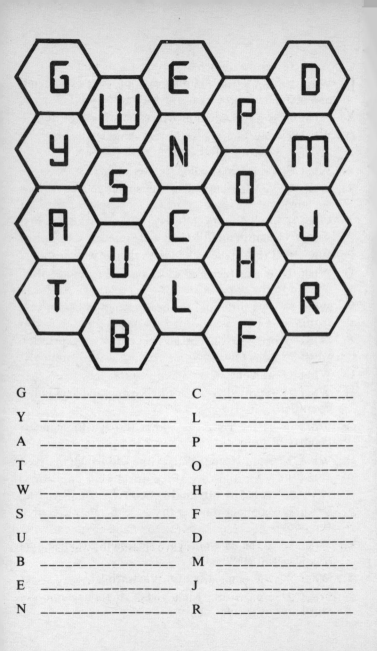

G _____ C _____

Y _____ L _____

A _____ P _____

T _____ O _____

W _____ H _____

S _____ F _____

U _____ D _____

B _____ M _____

E _____ J _____

N _____ R _____

G: What 'G' is divided in two and produces hock and sauerkraut?

Y: What 'Y' is a tree often planted in graveyards?

A: What 'A' is a fruit known also as an alligator pear?

T: What 'T' is a rose prickle?

W: What 'W' was responsible for the design of fifty-one London churches?

S: What 'S' is the wire fastener that holds a booklet together through the centrefold?

U: What 'U' is a little ragamuffin and is applied to a type of short haircut?

B: What 'B' is a kind of coarse fern that infests heath, moorland and mountain?

E: What 'E' comes after electric, sand and conger?

N: What 'N' do you mean to hit with a hammer, but also often hit by mistake?

C: What 'C' is the type of crow that feeds on dead animals?

L: What 'L' are you not in when you are fancy-free?

P: What 'P' is Scottish or American for the little finger, or a character in 'Brighton Rock'?

O: What 'O' is Des, whose best known song was 'Careless Hands'?

H: What 'H' is an eleven-a-side game played with curved sticks?

F: What 'F' is the art of planting, managing, and tending great numbers of trees?

D: What 'D' comes before horse, ages and continent?

M: What 'M' is a book which gave clues to the whereabouts of a jewelled hare?

J: What 'J' is the profession of collection and writing news?

R: What 'R' is where you can occasionally find a stationary taxi?

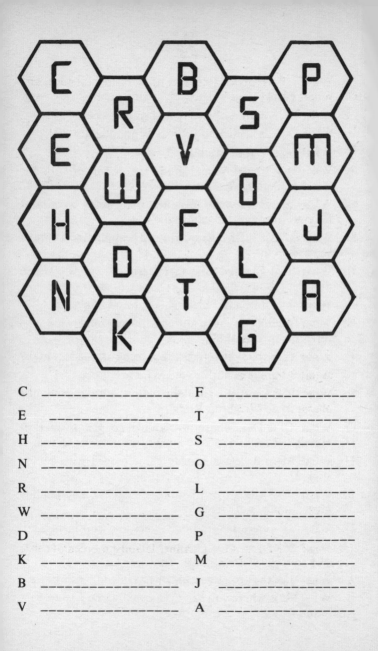

C	_____	F	_____
E	_____	T	_____
H	_____	S	_____
N	_____	O	_____
R	_____	L	_____
W	_____	G	_____
D	_____	P	_____
K	_____	M	_____
B	_____	J	_____
V	_____	A	_____

C: What 'C' is the game in which Emmanuel Lasker was supreme?

E: What 'E' is the period between afternoon and night?

H: What 'H' is the largest of London's Royal parks?

N: What 'N' had an ark and led animals in two by two?

R: What 'R' is mass for the repose of the souls of the dead?

W: What 'W' is the family of trees to which the osiers and sallows belong?

D: What 'D' is usually shown by a red signal and means beware?

K: What 'K' is an Australian bear?

B: What 'B' is the colour that in this country signifies mourning?

V: What 'V' is a tax?

F: What 'F' is the tree that shows your genealogy?

T: What 'T' in Staffordshire gave its name to Peel's manifesto in 1834?

S: What 'S' is a post for marking out territory, or is money placed in a bet?

O: What 'O' was called Daniel and was the early 19th century leader of Irish Nationalism?

L: What 'L' are German songs?

G: What 'G' has a district called 'Pollock'?

P: What 'P' is a hundredth part of a German Mark?

M: What 'M' did Burns address as a 'Wee, sleekit, cowering, timorous beastie'?

J: What 'J' is part of the Channel Islands, a breed of cattle and an article of clothing?

A: What 'A' is kept in an urn at Lords?

F _____

O _____

I _____

R _____

T _____

A _____

E _____

B _____

P _____

D _____

N _____

J _____

S _____

H _____

V _____

G _____

M _____

W _____

C _____

L _____

25

F: What 'F' is an ordinal of one?

O: What 'O' is a child without parents?

I: What 'I' lights up?

R: What 'R' is commemorated on Easter Sunday?

T: What 'T' is thirteen plus fourteen minus fifteen?

A: What 'A' is the science, or art, in which the adjective 'palladian' is used?

E: What 'E' are two and two and two and two?

B: What 'B' includes the Medulla oblongate, the pons and the cerebellum?

P: What 'P' was Marshal of France and head of Vichy Government during the last war?

D: What 'D' borrowed four million pounds to buy shares in the Suez Canal Company?

N: What 'N' is a sandbank with a lightship near Sheerness that was the scene of a famous mutiny?

J: What 'J' is the bone in which teeth are set?

S: What 'S' is what you are told to pull up when your performance has been substandard?

H: What 'H' is the opposite of perpendicular?

V: What 'V' does something do when it quivers and shakes?

G: What 'G' is the ham of a hog and goes proverbially with spinach?

M: What 'M' is a single block of stone like a menhir?

W: What 'W' are you when you are tired?

C: What 'C' is the BBC's teletext service?

L: What 'L' was the name of three kings of Belgium?

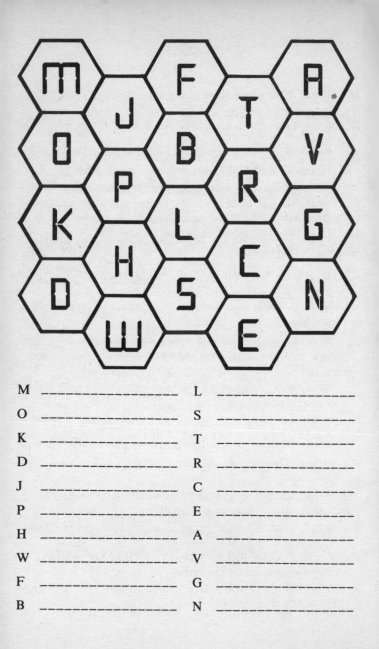

M	_____	L	_____
O	_____	S	_____
K	_____	T	_____
D	_____	R	_____
J	_____	C	_____
P	_____	E	_____
H	_____	A	_____
W	_____	V	_____
F	_____	G	_____
B	_____	N	_____

26

M: What 'M' is a northern town once known as 'Cotton-opolis'?

O: What 'O' is the surname of Scarlett in 'Gone with the Wind'?

K: What 'K' is an instrument for winding, turning, tightening and locking?

D: What 'D' was Britain's first Jewish Prime Minister?

J: What 'J' is applied to a prejudiced eye that sees only faults like that of a person with an upset liver?

P: What 'P' goes before chair, bike and button?

H: What 'H' is that part of Hispaniola that isn't Dominica, and is the home of voodoo?

W: What 'W' is a battle that forms the backdrop of episodes in Thackeray's 'Vanity Fair'?

F: What 'F' is an ancient implement for threshing corn?

B: What 'B' was the youngest and favourite son of Jacob?

L: What 'L' is the milky fluid produced by many plants, such as poppies and lettuce, but specially by the rubber plant?

S: What 'S' is the sport with which Australian Geoff Hunt is chiefly associated?

T: What 'T' is the Republic whose capital city is T'ai-pei?

R: What 'R' do you 'bring up' when you are right at the back?

C: What 'C' is the red pepper made from chillis?

E: What 'E' is the age at which you can vote in Britain?

A: What 'A' was the wife of silly Billy, who succeeded George and preceded Victoria?

V: What 'V' was the name of Britain's entry in the 1984 Americas Cup race?

G: What 'G' was eighty in 1984, wrote 'Our Man in Havana' and was christened Graham?

N: What 'N' was the place where Charles 1 lost the Midlands to Fairfax?

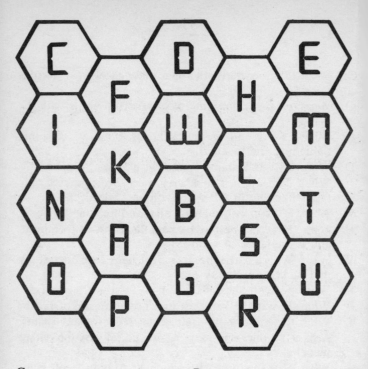

C _____   B _____

I _____   G _____

N _____   H _____

O _____   L _____

F _____   S _____

K _____   R _____

A _____   E _____

P _____   M _____

D _____   T _____

W _____   U _____

27

C: What 'C' is the country with the second largest area in the world?

I: What 'I' is the peninsular which was a theatre of war against the French?

N: What 'N' is the acid whose formula is HNO_3?

O: What 'O' supplies the feathers for the Prince of Wales' crest?

F: What 'F' was the saint associated with Assisi?

K: What 'K' from Australia is called a 'laughing Jackass'?

A: What 'A' was the Liberal leader whose second wife was called Margot?

P: What 'P' is where one sometimes has to put one's pride?

D: What 'D' live in columbarium?

W: What 'W' goes before pepper, lie and elephant?

B: What 'B' do mammals have platelets or thrombocytes?

G: What 'G' is the network of lines used for locating points on a map?

H: What 'H' did John Jorrocks call 'The sport of Kings – the image of war without its guilt'?

L: What 'L' is a self-propelled vehicle, particularly a railway engine?

S: What 'S' goes before man, line and jacket?

R: What 'R' is another name for the breakdance called 'The Mannequin'?

E: What 'E' do you raise as a sign of surprise or shock?

M: What 'M' was Uncas, the last chief, according to Fennimore Cooper?

T: What 'T' was the Sherpa who first climbed Everest?

U: What 'U' is the special bread eaten by the Jews which contains no yeast?

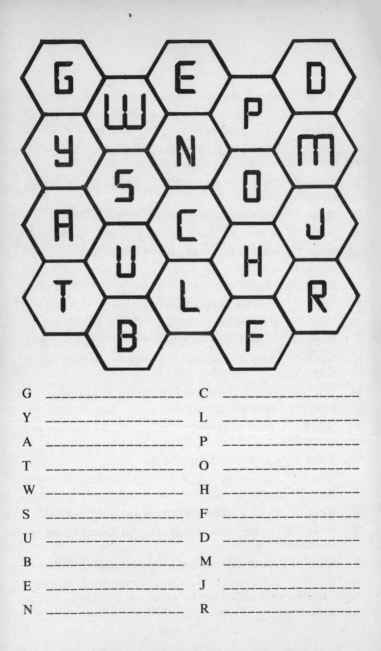

G	_____	C	_____
Y	_____	L	_____
A	_____	P	_____
T	_____	O	_____
W	_____	H	_____
S	_____	F	_____
U	_____	D	_____
B	_____	M	_____
E	_____	J	_____
N	_____	R	_____

28

G: What 'G' do you do in a betting shop?

Y: What 'Y' is a television programme about a group of students?

A: What 'A' is wilful setting-on-fire of property, often with the object of gain from the insurance?

T: What 'T' is the hero of a world famous comic strip for children created by Hergé?

W: What 'W' is the site of the Thames flood barrier?

S: What 'S' do you use to catch a mackerel?

U: What 'U' is where a female goat or sheep keeps its milk?

B: What 'B' is where your heart goes when you get that sinking feeling?

E: What 'E' is a way of identifying something you intend for a special purpose – like one of your own animals?

N: What 'N' is what a baby wears that needs constant changing?

C: What 'C' is the standard unit of heat?

L: What 'L' provides bits called 'best end' and 'saddle'?

P: What 'P' is the supposed science of deducing character by feeling the bumps on the head?

O: What 'O' are the bandits that are fruit machines?

H: What 'H' is a group of birds, proverbially said to have very good sight?

F: What 'F' are toadstools and penicillin?

D: What 'D' is a notorious sand bank in the North Sea?

M: What 'M' is the unlawful killing of one person by another?

J: What 'J' is reserved when a decision is delayed after a trial?

R: What 'R' was the method by which the British electorate decided we should join the EEC?

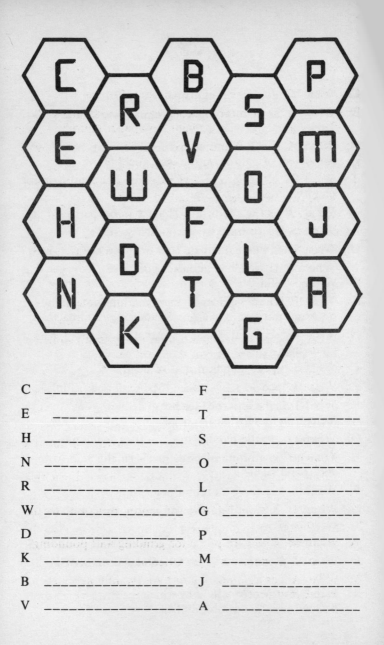

C _____ F _____

E _____ T _____

H _____ S _____

N _____ O _____

R _____ L _____

W _____ G _____

D _____ P _____

K _____ M _____

B _____ J _____

V _____ A _____

29

C: What 'C' is a large country house in France?

E: What 'E' is the Harold who wrote 'Good Times, Bad Times' and was once a major newspaper editor?

H: What 'H' is a mongrel or crossbreed?

N: What 'N' is a seamstress or embroiderer?

R: What 'R' is pink, and stewed, and is what actors in crowd scenes are supposed to mumble?

W: What 'W' is the Sunday that can be May 10, at the earliest, and June 23, at the latest?

D: What 'D' is our name for German porcelain shepherdesses, which actually came from Meissen?

K: What 'K' is the bone joint at the base of the finger?

B: What 'B' comes before alley, corner, and date?

V: What 'V' is a very soft silken fabric?

F: What 'F' is a derogatory word for things easily done, or for a ready, fluent way of doing things?

T: What 'T' are the Separatist group in Sri Lanka?

S: What 'S' is a horse-race over obstacles, or a race for men over hurdles and water-jumps?

O: What 'O' is a child without brothers and sisters?

L: What 'L' was written by Shirley Conran and is about a woman trying to identify her mother?

G: What 'G' is to chew away at something like a dog with a bone?

P: What 'P' is complete loss of motor function, in the nervous system?

M: What 'M' goes with pestle for grinding and pounding?

J: What 'J' is rubbish and an Oriental sailing boat?

A: What 'A' has a population of over 5¼ million, and is an island continent?

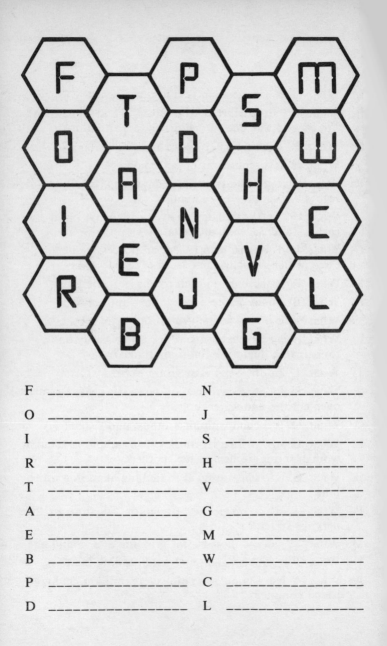

F _____   N _____

O _____   J _____

I _____   S _____

R _____   H _____

T _____   V _____

A _____   G _____

E _____   M _____

B _____   W _____

P _____   C _____

D _____   L _____

30

F: What 'F' comes before tale, ring and cake?

O: What 'O' are international games held in a different country every four years?

I: What 'I' is a pause or break?

R: What 'R' is the system of support and the ropes for moving sails on a ship?

T: What 'T' is what a compositor sets?

A: What 'A' is the process of cutting off an arm or a leg?

E: What 'E' were the people who had a principal deity called Osiris?

B: What 'B' was the scene of history's most famous tea party?

P: What 'P' is a mixture of flour, fat and water, rolled and used for pies and tarts?

D: What 'D' is the process by which food is converted into substances that can be absorbed into the blood?

N: What 'N' is the study of coins and medals?

J: What 'J' is a famous psychologist?

S: What 'S' is the Russian for 'Fellow-traveller', and the name given to their first artificial satellites?

H: What 'H' is usually mentioned as the second of the three theological virtues?

V: What 'V' is an innoculation against disease?

G: What 'G' do you see in skeins and gaggles?

M: What 'M' in London is 202 feet high, and commemorates the Great Fire?

W: What 'W' are birds that are pied and grey?

C: What 'C' did Mrs Malaprop really mean when she referred to the 'Allegories of the Nile' (because her English was as peculiar as her knowledge of natural history)?

L: What 'L' means noisy?

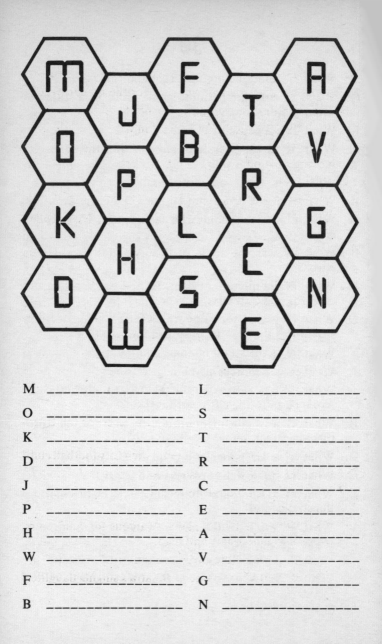

M _____   L _____

O _____   S _____

K _____   T _____

D _____   R _____

J _____   C _____

P _____   E _____

H _____   A _____

W _____   V _____

F _____   G _____

B _____   N _____

31

M: What 'M' is a two-syllable word for the human race?

O: What 'O' is the value rating for petrol?

K: What 'K' is the recoil of a shotgun or rifle?

D: What 'D' is the eider that produces eiderdown?

J: What 'J' are the calendars that begin with 'Nisan' for the church and 'Tishni' for civil affairs?

P: What 'P' do mice do when the cat's away?

H: What 'H' do falconers fly at small game?

W: What 'W' is a very difficult breakdance move that might grind the corn?

F: What 'F' is how one would like to be in a foreign language and means a ready use of words?

B: What 'B' is where Queen Elizabeth is Head of State, and where Nassau is the principal city?

L: What 'L' was, and is, the German Airforce?

S: What 'S' was the host nation for the final tournament of the World Cup in 1982?

T: What 'T' is a loudspeaker for reproducing high frequencies?

R: What 'R' was originally a political label for the Ultra-liberals, which we now call the Left?

C: What 'C' is the nickname for Norwich City football club?

E: What 'E' has a winter resort on the river at Luxor?

A: What 'A' is an animal found in South Africa called a klipspringer?

V: What 'V' was a Dutch painter, famous for sunflowers, whose surname was Van Gogh?

G: What 'G' goes before eye, fleece and rod?

N: What 'N' is the first name of Sinatra's singing daughter?

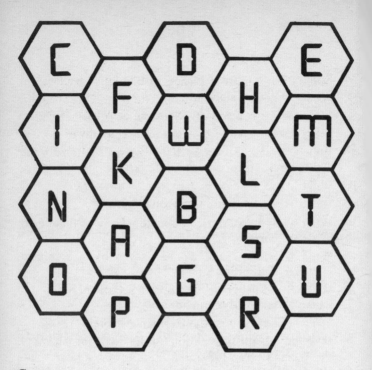

C _____   B _____

I _____   G _____

N _____   H _____

O _____   L _____

F _____   S _____

K _____   R _____

A _____   E _____

P _____   M _____

D _____   T _____

W _____   U _____

32

C: What 'C' is a heap of stones, or a Scottish terrier?

I: What 'I' wrote 'Fools are in a terrible, overwhelming majority all the wide world over', and was Norway's greatest dramatist?

N: What 'N' was a twenty franc piece named after an emperor?

O: What 'O' is the longest river in South Africa?

F: What 'F' is a flat slab of rock, an iris, or a piece of bunting used as a signal?

K: What 'K' is used of difficult problems or of a string tied in several places?

A: What 'A' is the Dutch language of South Africa?

P: What 'P' do you establish with a plumb line?

D: What 'D' is what American soldiers in the First World War were called?

W: What 'W' is a town in Hampshire with a cathedral, and a table said to be King Arthur's?

B: What 'B' comes before rate, and note, and after piggy?

G: What 'G' is an instrument called a stratocaster?

H: What 'H' is the Cinque Port that isn't Hastings?

L: What 'L' had a thorn removed from its foot by Androcles?

S: What 'S' goes before interest, fracture and minds?

R: What 'R' was the name of the monk who dominated the court of Nicholas II of Russia?

E: What 'E' was the name given to children sent away from big cities for safety during the last war?

M: What 'M' is characteristically guilty of the sin of avarice?

T: What 'T' is a polyester fibre noted for its non-creasing properties?

U: What 'U' is another word for the Cosmos?

G _____   C _____

Y _____   L _____

A _____   P _____

T _____   O _____

W _____   H _____

S _____   F _____

U _____   D _____

B _____   M _____

E _____   J _____

N _____   R _____

33

G: What 'G' is the principal city in Lake Leman?

Y: What 'Y' is an American university and a type of lock?

A: What 'A' is the region round the North Pole?

T: What 'T' goes before clap, bolt and storm?

W: What 'W' was the heathen god who gave his name to Wednesday?

S: What 'S' was the canal built by De Lesseps in Egypt?

U: What 'U' is a final demand or a threat?

B: What 'B' is what some people can't say to a goose?

E: What 'E' is a grossly excessive or extortionate price or demand?

N: What 'N' is a string of beads?

C: What 'C' is a perforated strainer for getting water out of vegetables?

L: What 'L' was the party of the red rose during the Wars of the Roses?

P: What 'P' goes before apple, marten and cone?

O: What 'O' is a hazard that arises out of your work, or what you habitually do?

H: What 'H' is the flat bit at the end of a nail?

F: What 'F' is the colloquial name for a note worth 500 pence?

D: What 'D' is to reduce in rank or importance?

M: What 'M' comes before field, storm and pole?

J: What 'J' was the wife of Punch?

R: What 'R' is a coloured arc which has something in common with Finian?

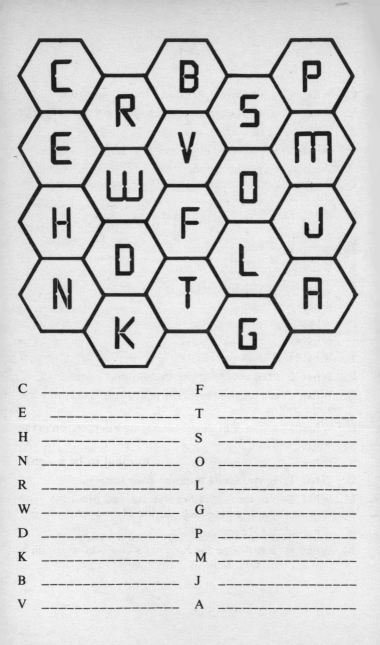

C _____
E _____
H _____
N _____
R _____
W _____
D _____
K _____
B _____
V _____

F _____
T _____
S _____
O _____
L _____
G _____
P _____
M _____
J _____
A _____

34

C: What 'C' is something arranged in order of time?

E: What 'E' is a ballet dancer's leap, during which the legs are rapidly crossed?

H: What 'H' is beautiful when it is calligraphy?

N: What 'N' is the Roman Deity identified with Poseidon?

R: What 'R' is the animal class that includes tortoises, crocodiles and snakes?

W: What 'W' is to talk under your breath, or in an undertone?

D: What 'D' is silly nonsense, or twaddle?

K: What 'K' is a Scottish church?

B: What 'B' is an exchange of goods, insead of money?

V: What 'V' are rats, mice and fleas?

F: What 'F' is an Italian city almost destroyed by flood in 1966?

T: What 'T' is the aquatic larval state of most amphibians?

S: What 'S' is the favourite slang name for the potato?

O: What 'O' means thoroughly stupid and is also applied to angles?

L: What 'L' is a sheet of water, occupying a depression in the earth's surface?

G: What 'G' was mustard with mutton said to be a sign?

P: What 'P' is said to be mightier than the sword?

M: What 'M' is the name we use for the Moslems who invaded Spain, and sometimes for Moroccans?

J: What 'J' did Romeo love?

A: What 'A' is a bridge for carrying water across a valley, that the Romans built in many places?

F _____   N _____

O _____   J _____

I _____   S _____

R _____   H _____

T _____   V _____

A _____   G _____

E _____   M _____

B _____   W _____

P _____   C _____

D _____   L _____

35

F: What 'F' is the verb for a sow giving birth to a litter of piglets?

O: What 'O' is a colour, an oil and something that can be eaten?

I: What 'I' is the part of the body where food is digested?

R: What 'R' is the Army bugle-call for waking soldiers?

T: What 'T' are the plants with which Bill Mason has to struggle?

A: What 'A' was Socialist Prime Minister in 1945?

E: What 'E' is a plain-coloured flag with a Union Jack in the corner?

B: What 'B' was the ship whose crew colonised Pitcairn Island, before they burned the ship?

P: What 'P' were Socrates, Descartes, Bertrand Russell and Wittgenstein?

D: What 'D' is the way a particular community within a county speaks?

N: What 'N' is a work of fiction writing?

J: Which 'J' is always running away from Tom?

S: What 'S' did the Rolling Stones not get?

H: What 'H' is a chart said to be 'cast' by an astrologer?

V: What 'V' was a Scandinavian seaman or pirate?

G: What 'G' was imprisoned for saying that the earth moved?

M: What 'M' was created on the fourth day?

W: What 'W' is a thin cake of batter, is cooked with an iron, and also means talking rubbish?

C: What 'C' is in charge of gambling games in a casino?

L: What 'L' is a black bootlace you can eat?

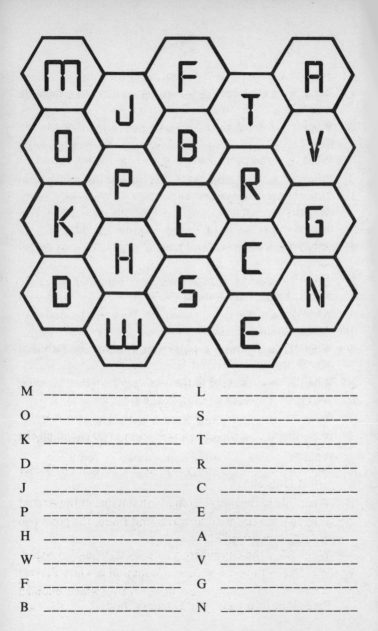

M _____   L _____

O _____   S _____

K _____   T _____

D _____   R _____

J _____   C _____

P _____   E _____

H _____   A _____

W _____   V _____

F _____   G _____

B _____   N _____

36

M: What 'M' is the planet fourth from the Sun?

O: What 'O' was the port near which uranium hexafluoride containers were sunk in a French boat?

K: What 'K' is a tower stronghold, usually square?

D: What 'D' is a tubular wooden Australian wind instrument?

J: What 'J' is an umbrella-shaped fish, called a Medusa, that stings?

P: What 'P' is a flat-bottomed boat, or a type of kick in rugby?

H: What 'H' is a woman who has, or is going to inherit a lot of money?

W: What 'W' goes before cub, hound or whistle?

F: What 'F' can be in kettles, on coat collars or on an unhealthy tongue?

B: What 'B' is the ecclesiastical boss of a diocese?

L: What 'L' is a country smaller than Washington DC, that lies between Switzerland and Austria?

S: What 'S' is used to cut grass, and appears with a hammer on the Soviet flag?

T: What 'T' is the great river on which Newcastle stands?

R: What 'R' is a cattle-breeding station in Canada and the USA?

C: What 'C' was the country that had a communist leader called Dubcek?

E: What 'E' are the native human inhabitants of the Arctic?

A: What 'A' makes, with Socrates and Plato, the great trio of Greek philosophy?

V: What 'V' is the city where you see the Bridge of Sighs?

G: What 'G' is the professional occupation of Gary Player?

N: What 'N' was chained up in the yard, which enabled Peter Pan to get into the Darlings' house?

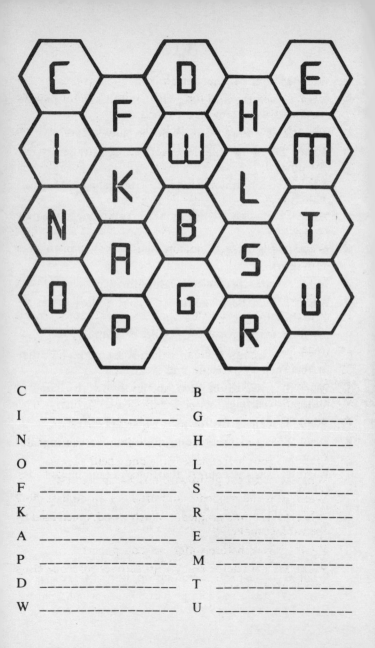

C _____

I _____

N _____

O _____

F _____

K _____

A _____

P _____

D _____

W _____

B _____

G _____

H _____

L _____

S _____

R _____

E _____

M _____

T _____

U _____

37

C: What 'C' is a vegetable with a large, white, edible flower-head?

I: What 'I' is one of the Balearic islands that live on importing tourists and exporting salt?

N: What 'N' is the English county that includes Ainwich and Bamburgh castles?

O: What 'O' is commonplace or usual?

F: What 'F' means a silly person when preceding brain, pate or head?

K: What 'K' is a small falcon that is also known as a windhover?

A: What 'A' is the Balkan communist state adjoining Greece?

P: What 'P' is the fruit called Kaki in Asia, that looks a bit like a tomato and figures in American folk stories?

D: What 'D' is an author of plays?

W: What 'W' is occidental?

B: What 'B' goes before pipe, up and lamp?

G: What 'G' is the nickname for the Royal Artillery?

H: What 'H' can be ball-pane, tack, sledge or claw?

L: What 'L' is the British rugby union overseas touring side?

S: What 'S' goes before lane, mile and shell?

R: What 'R' is to cut grain with a sickle at harvest?

E: What 'E' is the residence and office of an ambassador?

M: What 'M' is a fine-grained, reddish wood, much used by the cabinet makers?

T: What 'T' goes before water, set and paper?

U: What 'U' is an actor ready to take over someone else's part in an emergency?

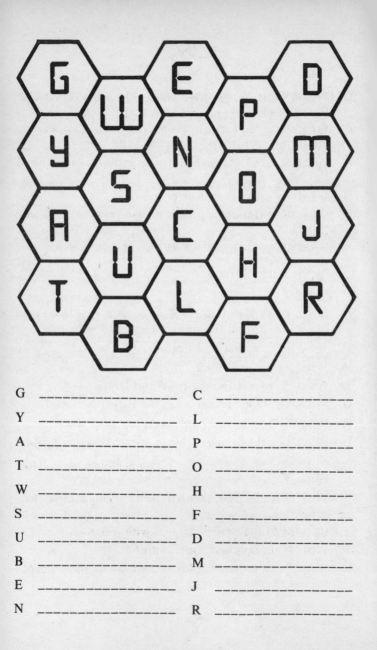

G _____ C _____

Y _____ L _____

A _____ P _____

T _____ O _____

W _____ H _____

S _____ F _____

U _____ D _____

B _____ M _____

E _____ J _____

N _____ R _____

38

G: What 'G' is the carriage on which the coffins of soldiers and statesmen are often transported?

Y: What 'Y' is a monetary unit of Japan's currency?

A: What 'A' are mountains that form a range entirely in Italy?

T: What 'T' is the number made by multiplying a hundred by ten?

W: What 'W' is the abbey owned by the Duke of Bedford?

S: What 'S' is a system of steps in a country wall or fence, where people, but not animals can cross?

U: What 'U' sits high up and gets abused by 'the brat of tennis'?

B: What 'B' comes after Christmas, witness and letter?

E: What 'E' is an aluminium cupid in Piccadilly?

N: What 'N' is a female goat or a child's nurse?

C: What 'C' is a deep blue pigment of metallic origin?

L: What 'L' is a sore throat in Latin?

P: What 'P' is the name of Edward Western closely linked with?

O: What 'O' means to acquire or get?

H: What 'H' is where Winston Churchill went to school?

F: What 'F' is the penalty that is an unchangeable fine for parking?

D: What 'D' is the cathedral in the north of England, started in 1093?

M: What 'M' could only be treated with quinine?

J: What 'J' are Split and Dubrovnik?

R: What 'R' were Flopsy, Mopsy, Cottontail and Peter?

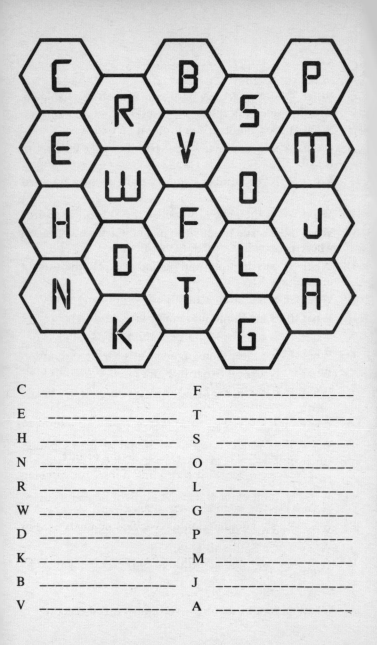

C _____   F _____

E _____   T _____

H _____   S _____

N _____   O _____

R _____   L _____

W _____   G _____

D _____   P _____

K _____   M _____

B _____   J _____

V _____   A _____

39

C: What 'C' is a thick, coarse fleshed, omnivorous river fish of the carp family?

E: What 'E' is the suffix meaning smaller imitation or female that can be added to flannel, usher or kitchen?

H: What 'H' is commonly used as a synonym for mesmerised?

N: What 'N' is the popular name for an allergic skin irritation called urticaria?

R: What 'R' is the versatile Mr Daltry, the pop star and actor?

W: What 'W' is spelt with an 'e' when it's Irish, and without when it's scotch?

D: What 'D' is the product of phoenix dactylifera that grows in the Near East?

K: What 'K' is a smoked herring?

B: What 'B' was the lump of wood on which people were beheaded?

V: What 'V' are blinds?

F: What 'F' was the name taken by a group of non-revolutionary socialists in England in 1884?

T: What 'T' is the art and science of fighting battles?

S: What 'S' is the saucepan in which bones are boiled to make the basis of soups and sauces?

O: What 'O' indicates the anti-knock rating of fuel?

L: What 'L' is a rope with a running noose, for catching cattle?

G: What 'G' is an engineless aeroplane?

P: What 'P' is a combination of specified numbers used in football pools?

M: What 'M' is the relationship of Princess Diana to Prince William?

J: What 'J' brings people bad luck?

A: What 'A' has, as its ore, a substance called bauxite?

F _____   N _____

O _____   J _____

I _____   S _____

R _____   H _____

T _____   V _____

A _____   G _____

E _____   M _____

B _____   W _____

P _____   C _____

D _____   L _____

40

F: What 'F' has a polypod got a lot of?

O: What 'O' is the edible home of a pearl?

I: What 'I' is important when applying for a job?

R: What 'R' was the French cardinal who was the virtual ruler of France in the early 17th century?

T: What 'T' means to wait, or delay, and rhymes with marry?

A: What 'A' is demanded for refugees and is a home for lunatics?

E: What 'E' is for ever and ever and ever?

B: What 'B' comes before spanner, room and office?

P: What 'P' is a traveller in a motor car who is not driving?

D: What 'D' in a pharmacy makes up the prescriptions?

N: What 'N' is a person or tribe who wanders from place to place?

J: What 'J' is a car and a big cat?

S: What 'S' is a ship designed to sail under the sea?

H: What 'H' is the full moon nearest the Autumn equinox?

V: What 'V' is the official residence of the Pope?

G: What 'G' is the element with the atomic number seventy-nine?

M: What 'M' in the Yemen is thought to have been the place where coffee originated?

W: What 'W' is a ballroom dance and one that Matilda did?

C: What 'C' can be a hen, lives in the sea and has pincers?

L: What 'L' was the husband of a woman in the bible who was turned into a pillar of salt?

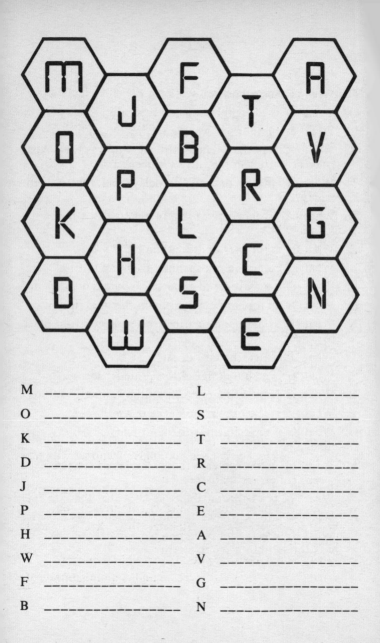

M _____ L _____

O _____ S _____

K _____ T _____

D _____ R _____

J _____ C _____

P _____ E _____

H _____ A _____

W _____ V _____

F _____ G _____

B _____ N _____

41

M: What 'M' is a name meaning pearl, given to a member of the Royal family?

O: What 'O' is the piece of music that opens an opera or oratorio?

K: What 'K' in Tanzania is the highest peak in Africa?

D: What 'D' wrote 'The Idiot' and 'The Brothers Karamazov'?

J: What 'J' is the triangular stay-sail, between the bowsprit and the masthead on a small boat?

P: What 'P' is the raised place in a church where the preacher delivers his sermon?

H: What 'H' was the mother of Hermione and caused the Trojan War?

W: What 'W' is the noise a horse makes when it is pleased?

F: What 'F' comes before body, office, country and legion?

B: What 'B' weighs 16¾ tons and is called 'Great Paul'?

L: What 'L' was once called St Petersburg, and is Russia's second city?

S: What 'S' is another word for a water-ice?

T: What 'T' is a thirteenth of twenty-six?

R: What 'R' is a fence of balustrade – often made of metal?

C: What 'C' was a Danish King of England who sat with his feet in the sea?

E: What 'E' is a print made from an engraved copper plate?

A: What 'A' is hard, dustfree, highly compressed coal?

V: What 'V' were Jascha Heifetz, Fritz Kreisler, and Paganini?

G: What 'G' are Welsh, Scots, Horse and Grenadier?

N: What 'N' is a kind of ice-cream and is an inhabitant of Naples?

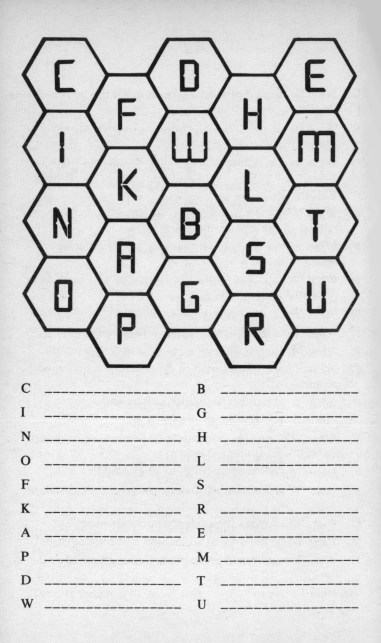

C _____ B _____

I _____ G _____

N _____ H _____

O _____ L _____

F _____ S _____

K _____ R _____

A _____ E _____

P _____ M _____

D _____ T _____

W _____ U _____

42

C: What 'C' is the vessel in which butter is made?

I: What 'I' is a house made of ice and snow?

N: What 'N' is the nickname usually given, in the navy or army, to someone called Clarke?

O: What 'O' are found at Kitt Peak, Mount Palomar and Jodrell Bank?

F: What 'F' do you add to thirty-three to get forty-seven?

K: What 'K' is the desert north of the Orange River, mostly in Botswana?

A: What 'A' is a plea of having been elsewhere at the material time?

P: What 'P' is government where a woman is dominant in the home of family life?

D: What 'D' is a light sleep?

W: What 'W' is the Duke commemorated at Apsley House?

B: What 'B' are you said to kick when you die?

G: What 'G' were Nepalese soldiers serving in the British Army?

H: What 'H' is a musical instrument (like a portable organ) with bellows worked by the feet?

L: What 'L' was originally made from flax, oil and corkdust, and is found in many kitchens?

S: What 'S' goes before string, hand and fiddle?

R: What 'R' is a vegetable that can be red, white, black or horse?

E: What 'E' supplies the evidence in ocular proof?

M: What 'M' is the animal studied by anthropologists?

T: What 'T' is stretched between the winning posts of a race-track?

U: What 'U' means on the first floor, or a higher storey?

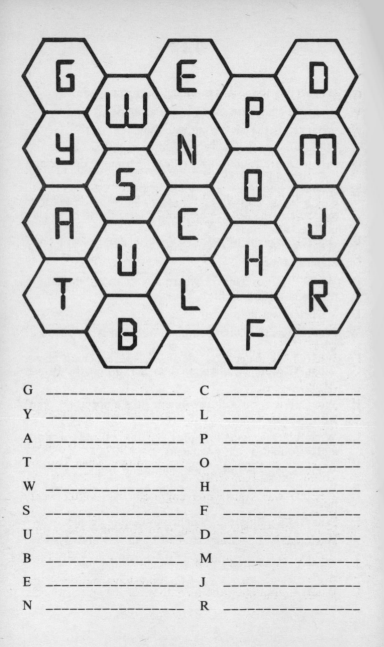

G _____   C _____

Y _____   L _____

A _____   P _____

T _____   O _____

W _____   H _____

S _____   F _____

U _____   D _____

B _____   M _____

E _____   J _____

N _____   R _____

43

G: What 'G' is between Honduras and Mexico?

Y: What 'Y' is the festive season of Christmas time?

A: What 'A' is vulnerable in the heel?

T: What 'T' is called a 'pourboire' or 'backsheesh'?

W: What 'W' does a bigamist have more than one of?

S: What 'S' did Aristotle think women hadn't got, and which most people think goes to heaven after death?

U: What 'U' goes before crust, cut and class?

B: What 'B' is the name given to a special gravy or sauce jug?

E: What 'E' is another word for an age, a period or an epoch?

N: What 'N' was a pig in 'Animal Farm', or emperor of France?

C: What 'C' are pale-coloured French beef cattle from near Lyons?

L: What 'L' is a decapod marine crustacean with claws, which is red when cooked?

P: What 'P' is the capital of Arizona?

O: What 'O' is the expression used to mean the time when the least electricity is used?

H: What 'H' do you fly-off if you get loquaciously angry?

F: What 'F' is used to knock you down when you are astonished and amazed?

D: What 'D' was Argus who recognised Ulysses after twenty years?

M: What 'M' was Sir Thomas who compiled the 'Morte D'Arthur'?

J: What 'J' is Lennon's pop musician son?

R: What 'R' was the king who may have murdered the princes in the tower?

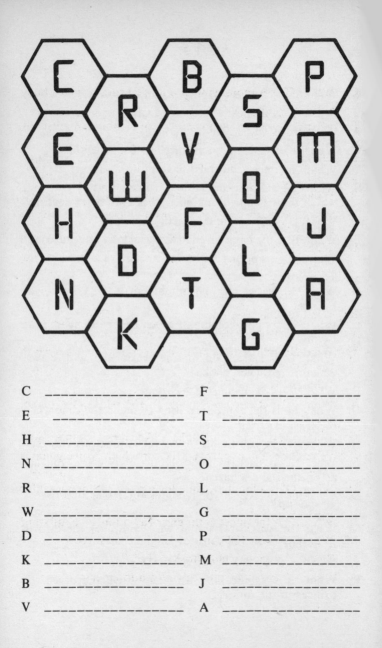

C _____

E _____

H _____

N _____

R _____

W _____

D _____

K _____

B _____

V _____

F _____

T _____

S _____

O _____

L _____

G _____

P _____

M _____

J _____

A _____

44

C: What 'C' is a monster with a lion's head, a goat's body and a dragon's tail?

E: What 'E' is an exaggerated feeling of well-being usually based on over-confidence?

H: What 'H' identified as 'IBN Talal' is King of Jordan?

N: What 'N' is the wine you mustn't put into old bottles?

R: What 'R' can be metamorphic, sedimentary, or igneous?

W: What 'W' is, or was, called baleen plate and was used in corsets and for brushes?

D: What 'D' is the disease you suffer from if you can't make your own insulin?

K: What 'K' is a famous diamond which weighs 102 carats and is one of the British crown jewels?

B: What 'B' can be a pole, an itch or a shop?

V: What 'V' is the poison secreted in snakes and bees?

F: What 'F' married the world's sweetheart and played in the 'Thief of Baghdad'?

T: What 'T' is a child's cuddly bear?

S: What 'S' is the correct name of the pedal of a piano, sometimes called the loud pedal?

O: What 'O' is a group of eight – like the notes in a scale?

L: What 'L' is a decorative textile for which Nottingham is famous?

G: What 'G' is a familiar name for a piece of linen used for drying-up?

P: What 'P' is the pause at the end of a sentence – a full stop?

M: What 'M' won 108 caps for England at soccer?

J: What 'J' was very close to Mr Hyde?

A: What 'A' are made into calvados and cider?

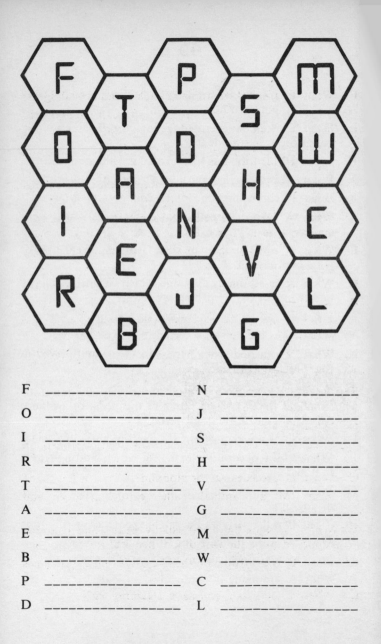

F _____ N _____

O _____ J _____

I _____ S _____

R _____ H _____

T _____ V _____

A _____ G _____

E _____ M _____

B _____ W _____

P _____ C _____

D _____ L _____

45

F: What 'F' are rockets, roman candles, and bengal lights?

O: What 'O' appears in a newspaper after a person's death?

I: What 'I' is the 'I' to which Moses led his people?

R: What 'R' is a din, an organised swindle, or a thing you play games with?

T: What 'T' is a person employed to judge the quality of tea or wine?

A: What 'A' was the Prince of Saxe Coburg Gotha who married Queen Victoria?

E: What 'E' are you said to walk on when you go very gingerly for some reason?

B: What 'B' is reed-mace, among which Moses was laid?

P: What 'P' is the important prison on the Isle of Wight?

D: What 'D' were the reptiles dominant during the Mesozoic period?

N: What 'N' is a prize for physics, literature and peace?

J: What 'J' was the wife of Napoleon?

S: What 'S' was a tube-like dress, of the early 50s, or a cloth container for potatoes?

H: What 'H' are dried in an oasthouse?

V: What 'V' is the zodiacal sign for someone born on September 1st?

G: What 'G' precedes ray or globulin?

M: What 'M' are animals called capuchin, green and marmoset?

W: What 'W' does the bride usually wear white at and is supposed to be the best day of her life?

C: What 'C' is the tropic on the line of latitude 23½ degrees north?

L: What 'L' are you if you have a gammy leg?

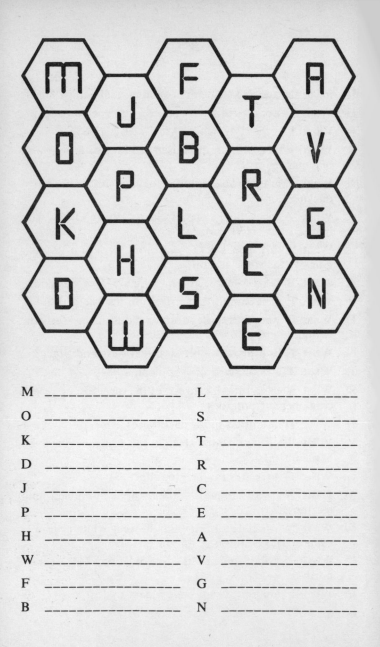

M _____   L _____

O _____   S _____

K _____   T _____

D _____   R _____

J _____   C _____

P _____   E _____

H _____   A _____

W _____   V _____

F _____   G _____

B _____   N _____

46

M: What 'M' is made of Seville oranges and eaten for breakfast?

O: What 'O' is a thorough examination with remedies or repairs if necessary?

K: What 'K' are the gloves to use for handling something very gingerly?

D: What 'D' had the names, John Juddam, as well as the 'Charles' by which he is world famous?

J: What 'J' is an object of laughter – a joke?

P: What 'P' means to poke with a stick or other object?

H: What 'H' was chancellor of Germany before Hitler?

W: What 'W' goes before nut, chair and commander?

F: What 'F' is the last part of an opera, or a musical and is often grand?

B: What 'B' comes in the form of silverside, skirt and shin?

L: What 'L' follows Burke's, Gresham's and Boyle's?

S: What 'S' goes before dog, scout and captain?

T: What 'T' in Italy has kept a shroud for many years?

R: What 'R' is used for shaving?

C: What 'C' is a salad-plant whose roasted roots make a coffee substitute?

E: What 'E' comes before drum, wig and ache?

A: What 'A' is another name for a motor car?

V: What 'V' was a man who governed a country in the name of its ruler, especially in the British Empire?

G: What 'G' is pickled and is like a little cucumber?

N: What 'N' is another word for the renal, meaning 'of the kidneys'?

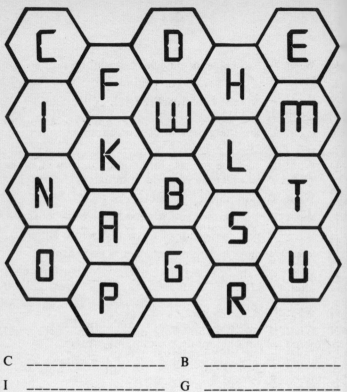

C _____   B _____

I _____   G _____

N _____   H _____

O _____   L _____

F _____   S _____

K _____   R _____

A _____   E _____

P _____   M _____

D _____   T _____

W _____   U _____

47

C: What 'C' is called a heifer when young?

I: What 'I' is a holy statue or picture?

N: What 'N' created the French Legion of Honour?

O: What 'O' is a padded chest (used as a seat) or a Turk of the 13th century?

F: What 'F' is six times twelves, minus thirty-two?

K: What 'K' is another word for paraffin?

A: What 'A' was christened 'Phoebe Ann Moses', and called 'Little Sureshot' by Sitting Bull?

P: What 'P' succeeded in taming the shrew?

D: What 'D' is needed to play chuck-a-luck or acey deucey?

W: What 'W' is the pot that never boils?

B: What 'B' is the all-girl group consisting of Sarah, Siobhan and Karen?

G: What 'G' is the inclination of a slope?

H: What 'H' comes before ghost, grail and Roman Empire?

L: What 'L' is a brown, soaring bird?

S: What 'S' is the Persian word for king?

R: What 'R' is measured by a Pluviometer?

E: What 'E' get about (and hunt) in a Kayak?

M: What 'M' is the common wild duck?

T: What 'T' sang 'On the Good Ship Lollipop', when she was about seven, and was called Shirley?

U: What 'U' is the anointing with Holy oil of a dying person?

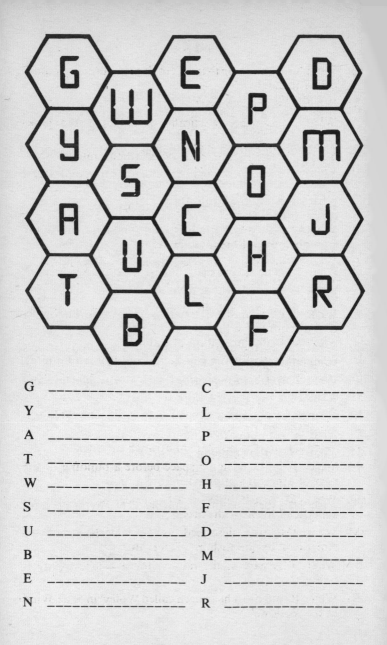

G _____

Y _____

A _____

T _____

W _____

S _____

U _____

B _____

E _____

N _____

C _____

L _____

P _____

O _____

H _____

F _____

D _____

M _____

J _____

R _____

48

G: What 'G' is the syrup that isn't molasses, but is sometimes called treacle?

Y: What 'Y' is spun thread?

A: What 'A' is characteristically white-haired and pink-eyed?

T: What 'T' is indicated by an 'M' in roman numerals?

W: What 'W' is the best known product of Orvieto in Italy?

S: What 'S' is a person who gets blamed for everything?

U: What 'U' was Grecian and addressed by Keats?

B: What 'B' is the symbol of happiness, and the name of the Campbell record-breaking boats?

E: What 'E' when it's fair is said to be 'No robbery'?

N: What 'N' is the part of a church often referred to as the aisle?

C: What 'C' is the master of a merchant ship, or the pilot of a civil aircraft?

L: What 'L' is the adjective applied to Robin Hood's companion John?

P: What 'P' is an adjective often used with elephant, eye and Floyd?

O: What 'O' was ranked second only to the emerald, as a gemstone, by the Romans?

H: What 'H' are the pointers of a watch or clock?

F: What 'F' is the enclosed space before a building or the part of a petrol station where the pumps are?

D: What 'D' is a dabbler in art, science, or literature, a superficial lover of the arts?

M: What 'M' was described as an 'elderly, imported American' by the Bishop of Durham?

J: What 'J' is part of the railway for which Clapham is famous?

R: What 'R' ought to have been called 'Voley' in 'The Wind in the Willows'?

C _____
E _____
H _____
N _____
R _____
W _____
D _____
K _____
B _____
V _____

F _____
T _____
S _____
O _____
L _____
G _____
P _____
M _____
J _____
A _____

49

C: What 'C' is mixed with zinc to make brass?

E: What 'E' is one of the seven deadly sins?

H: What 'H' is an extremely large and rather uncommon wasp?

N: What 'N' is the bomb designed to kill people rather than damage buildings?

R: What 'R' are: Ena Harkness, Josephine Bruce and Coral Cluster?

W: What 'W' wrote 'The Time Machine' and 'Ann Veronica'?

D: What 'D' is a small furrow for seeds, or a tool for making holes?

K: What 'K' is the Muslim prayer book?

B: What 'B' is a male pig?

V: What 'V' are dilated or enlarged veins, usually in the legs?

F: What 'F' do you take to something you suddenly find you like?

T: What 'T' wears a frill with bells to frighten away the devil, is an entertaining dog, and is also a jug?

S: What 'S' is an everyday name for an accordion?

O: What 'O' are a pair of socks that don't match in colour?

L: What 'L' are caterpillars, grubs and tadpoles?

G: What 'G' is a system for transferring credits between banks and post offices?

P: What 'P' is the main square in an Italian town?

M: What 'M' is the lawyer/writer called John, who created 'Rumpole' and many other characters?

J: What 'J' was the name of two of Henry VIII's wives?

A: What 'A' was the Greek conqueror who was educated by Aristotle?

F _____ N _____

O _____ J _____

I _____ S _____

R _____ H _____

T _____ V _____

A _____ G _____

E _____ M _____

B _____ W _____

P _____ C _____

D _____ L _____

50

F: What 'F' was pulled or waved in India by a punkah wallah?

O: What 'O' are kidneys, liver and heart when eaten?

I: What 'I' is applied to a person who dies without making a will?

R: What 'R' is a problem for dyslexics?

T: What 'T' is an old-fashioned term for a pub or inn?

A: What 'A' is a sport where 'A Gold' is the bullseye?

E: With what 'E' were Miss Beale and Miss Buss concerned?

B: What 'B' is a gesture of obeisance or respect?

P: What 'P' are soldiers dropped into positions from aeroplanes?

D: What 'D' is an amount deducted from the price of an article as an incentive to pay cash?

N: What 'N' is a musical sign, a short written communication and to observe something?

J: What 'J' is a wild member of the dog family?

S: What 'S' is finely sliced cabbage pickled in German style?

H: What 'H' is very cold rain and a greeting?

V: What 'V' is a pea, carrot, potato, but not a tomato?

G: What 'G' was a famous bearded doctor who for years dominated English cricket?

M: What 'M' is said to have been seen by a motorist in 1933 swimming in Loch Ness?

W: What 'W' is done by a dog when it is happy?

C: What 'C' is a little red fruit that makes the jelly that's eaten with turkey?

L: What 'L' was the favourite subject of the painter John Constable?

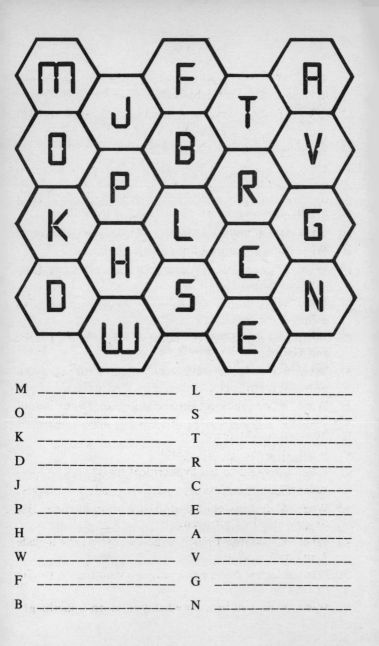

M _____ L _____

O _____ S _____

K _____ T _____

D _____ R _____

J _____ C _____

P _____ E _____

H _____ A _____

W _____ V _____

F _____ G _____

B _____ N _____

51

M: What 'M' is the name connected with anti-communist hysteria in the United States?

O: What 'O' is an emerging stratum of rock at the surface?

K: What 'K' wrote an ode on a 'Grecian Urn'?

D: What 'D' is a magistrate of Venice?

J: What 'J' was the Capulet who first drugged and then stabbed herself?

P: What 'P' is a word meaning a marvel, that is often applied to infants?

H: What 'H' are human beings, dogs and cats to fleas?

W: What 'W' was called the Iron Duke?

F: What 'F' are stories recounted or collected by Grimm, Andersen and Perrault?

B: What 'B' is the composer who means so much to Schroeder in 'Peanuts'?

L: What 'L' is a grand duchy bordered by Belgium, France and Germany?

S· What 'S' is the general name for British currency, and a standard for silver?

T: What 'T' was the occupation, study, or profession, of Niebuhr (pronounced Nee-boor) and Niemöller (pronounced Niemerler)?

R: What 'R' is the 'R' of USSR?

C: What 'C' is said to cry hypocritical tears?

E: What 'E' is a short journey to deliver goods or messages?

A: What 'A' consists chiefly of .03% carbon dioxide, 21% oxygen and 78% nitrogen?

V: What 'V' was the French writer whose works include 'Candide'?

G: What 'G' is the American evangelist who toured Britain in 1984?

N: What 'N' do you turn up when you scorn something?

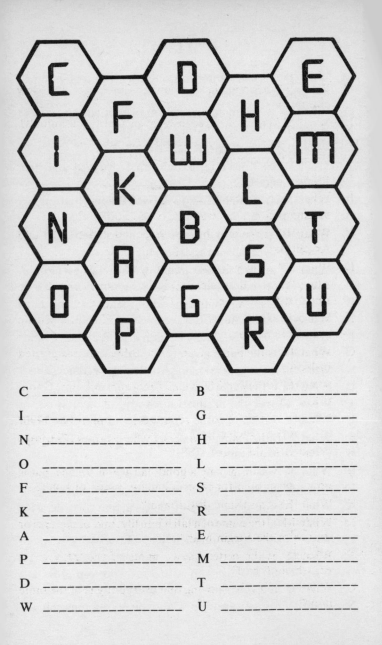

C _____   B _____

I _____   G _____

N _____   H _____

O _____   L _____

F _____   S _____

K _____   R _____

A _____   E _____

P _____   M _____

D _____   T _____

W _____   U _____

52

C: What 'C' is wood that has undergone smothered slow combustion?

I: What 'I' helps police reconstruct pictures of criminals?

N: What 'N' is the bespectacled Mouskouri?

O: What 'O' is to express disapproval?

F: What 'F' is lucre?

K: What 'K' is the Scottish word for cabbage?

A: What 'A' comes before tern, ocean and fox?

P: What 'P' is the unit of currency in Bolivia, Cuba and Argentina?

D: What 'D' is the currency of the USA?

W: What 'W' is one of the two ways in which iron can be smelted; the other being 'cast'?

B: What 'B' is the name of a flower and of a little private railway in Sussex?

G: What 'G' is the name given to the Bible that was printed in 1456?

H: What 'H' is the name by which Secombe, one-time Goon, is known?

L: What 'L' will have to be removed from petrol by 1990?

S: What 'S' is the plain in Somerset where James II's troops defeated Monmouth?

R: What 'R' was originally a gondola race in Venice, but is now a term used for races for many kinds of boats?

E: What 'E' is a seismic disturbance?

M: What 'M' is the name of a tall white lily, and of pictures or statues of the Virgin Mary?

T: What 'T' is the better known name of the 'Mavis' – a British song bird?

U: What 'U' is a vote showing that everybody is of the same mind?

G _____   C _____

Y _____   L _____

A _____   P _____

T _____   O _____

W _____   H _____

S _____   F _____

U _____   D _____

B _____   M _____

E _____   J _____

N _____   R _____

53

G: What 'G' are the four accounts of the life of Jesus in the Bible?

Y: What 'Y' is slang for American people?

A: What 'A' consists of the ionosphere, the stratosphere and the troposphere?

T: What 'T' is the heroine who goes with Pyramus?

W: What 'W' means scared, but is applied to the city of Chicago with a different sense?

S: What 'S' are fish that come tightly packed in tins?

U: What 'U' is 'beyond what is openly seen or known' and applied to motives?

B: What 'B' is part of a drill, or the mouthpiece of a bridle?

E: What 'E' was thought of by Alfred Russell at the same time as Darwin?

N: What 'N' was Macdonald's coalition government of 1931?

C: What 'C' is a soft head-covering with a peak, worn by schoolboys and sportsmen?

L: What 'L' are small rodents given to sudden disastrous migrations?

P: What 'P' goes before officer, fish and light?

O: What 'O' is a place where you can buy alcoholic drinks but can't consume them on the premises?

H: What 'H' has a famous dynasty that ruled Austria, Hungary and Bohemia?

F: What 'F' was the character based on Sir John Oldcastle by Shakespeare?

D: What 'D' are woad, tyrian purple and airline mauve?

M: What 'M' is a small creature that can beat a cobra?

J: What 'J' used to be a combat between knights on horseback?

R: What 'R' is the acronym for the best known theatre school in this country?

C _____
E _____
H _____
N _____
R _____
W _____
D _____
K _____
B _____
V _____

F _____
T _____
S _____
O _____
L _____
G _____
P _____
M _____
J _____
A _____

54

C: What 'C' is another name for a janitor and the name of a Pinter play?

E: What 'E' is the gas container of a balloon, or the cover for a letter?

H: What 'H' is the name given to the snail's tentacles, or a beetle's antenna?

N: What 'N' do you keep to the grindstone when kept hard at work?

R: What 'R' is another name for a carousel or merry-go-round?

W: What 'W' had a son called Sam, in a book by Dickens, and said, 'Be very careful o'viders all your life!'?

D: What 'D' is a primitive canoe made out of a hollowed tree trunk?

K: What 'K' is the material for and act of starting a fire?

B: What 'B' was the cathedral town invented and made famous by Trollope?

V: What 'V' is a surgeon who treats sick animals?

F: What 'F' is a largish bundle of sticks?

T: What 'T' is the first name of dramatist Stoppard?

S: What 'S' was a Thracian leader of rebellious slaves in 73 BC?

O: What 'O' is a poem meant to be sung, or else a long lyric in exalted style?

L: What 'L' was seen in a dream going up to heaven, by Jacob?

G: What 'G' is a reddish-yellow colour or a hot root?

P: What 'P' was an American Indian princess, who married an Englishman in the 16th century?

M: What 'M' do you get for jam or old rope?

J: What 'J' is a river running into the Dead Sea?

A: What 'A' is the sign of the zodiac for January 31st?

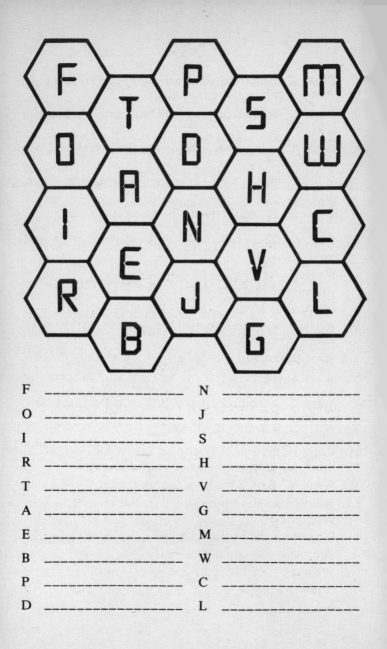

F _____
O _____
I _____
R _____
T _____
A _____
E _____
B _____
P _____
D _____

N _____
J _____
S _____
H _____
V _____
G _____
M _____
W _____
C _____
L _____

55

F: What 'F' is the square root of sixteen?

O: What 'O' is a rectangle?

I: What 'I' is in a pen?

R: What 'R' is another name for the disease hydrophobia?

T: What 'T' is an agreement for a temporary cessation of hostilities?

A: What 'A' were the pre-Raphaelite brotherhood?

E: What 'E' is the biblical name for paradise?

B: What 'B' was the town where the Liberals held their 1984 assembly?

P: What 'P' was used as writing material by the ancient Egyptians and was a form of sedge?

D: What 'D' is brown crystalline sugar?

N: What 'N' is a serviette used for wiping one's mouth or fingers when eating?

J: What 'J' is a bird that has an eye for glittering prizes?

S: What 'S' is a weekly or monthly payment in return for work?

H: What 'H' is a kind of bean?

V: What 'V' is a strict vegetarian?

G: What 'G' are pheasants, deer, partridges and grouse?

M: What 'M' precedes nature, love and courage?

W: What 'W' does a bowler aim at in cricket?

C: What 'C' is a clear, transparent, ice-like mineral – usually pure quartz?

L: What 'L' is the South American quadruped that spits?

Solution: Puzzle 1

M: Main; O: Outsize; K: Krishna; D: Daisy; J: June; P: Pound; H: Herring; W: Waller; F: Fault; B: 'Bewitched'; L: Lucy; S: Safari; T: Trumpet; R: Ranger; C: Cucumber; E: Edward (VII); A: Abbot; V: Violin; G: Grant; N: Navel.

Solution: Puzzle 2

C: Chain; I: Impact (ed); N: Nuffield; O: Over; F: Forget-me-not; K: Knock; A: Alec; P: Poland; D: Dirigibles; W: Whipped; B: Belafonte; G: Gout; H: Honduras; L: Longhaired; S: Scotch; R: Rag; E: Enigma; M: Moses; T: Thomas; U: Unicycle.

Solution: Puzzle 3

G: Glasgow; Y: Yacht; A: Advent; T: 'Thriller'; W: Wrong; S: Snoopy; U: Undergrowth; B: Buoy; E: Eye; N: Nib; C: Composer; L: Lenin; P: Persuasion; O: Oil; H: Hungry; F: Fish; D: Dime; M: Marvin; J: Jet; R: Receiver.

Solution: Puzzle 4

C: Chesterfield; E: Examinations; H: Happy; N: Neat; R: Racehorses; W: Windflower (Anemos is wind in Greek); D: David; K: Kindergarten; B: Bolivia; V: Valentine; F: Flurry; T: Teeth; S: Soliloquy; O: Olive; L: Left; G: Gossamer; P: Petal; M: Musicians; J: Jaffa; A: Auto.

Solution: Puzzle 5

F: Fluke; O: Obsession; I: Impedes; R: Rowing; T: Tay; A: Archer; E: Essex; B: Box; P: Perspiration; D: Darlington; N: Normandy; J: Jury; S: Sling; H: Hawk; V: Void; G: Gibraltar; M: Molasses; W: Witch; C: Cap; L: Lomond.

Solution: Puzzle 6

M: Manny; O: Outfield; K: Kennedy; D: Danton; J: Jitters; P: Polo; H: Homogenised; W: Wax; F: Fluke; B: Berlin; L: Luther; S: Sabbath; T: Tub; R: Rancid; C: Cupboard; E: Economics; A: Aberdeen; V: Venice; G: Grasshopper; N: New.

Solution: Puzzle 7

C: Cowans (Norman); I: Iodine; N: Newspapers; O: Ostler; F: Frogs; K: Kidnap; A: Alice; P: Portugal; D: Dingo; W: Walloons; B: Belgrade; G: Glamis; H: Healthy; L: Lobe; S: Screen; R: Rex; E: Exceed; M: Muslim; T: Trident; U: Unwind.

Solution: Puzzle 8

G: Gummer; Y: Yeast; A: Abracadabra; T: Terns; W: Wolf; S: Scarborough; U: Ubiquity; B: Brogue; E: Exhaustive; N: Nehru; C: Christopher; L: Leader; P: Phonograph; O: Onion; H: Hangar; F: Fir; D: Dinosaurs; M: Mark; J: Jilt; R: Recital.

Solution: Puzzle 9

C: Canvass; E: Eyes; H: Hawkmoth; N: Nebuchadnezzar; R: Race; W: Water; D: Dipstick; K: Kiosk; B: Berlin; V: Vulture; F: Forceps; T: Turk(ish); S: Spat; O: Olivier; L: Linen; G: Golfclubs; P: Paper; M: Mull; J: Jagger; A: Aegean.

Solution: Puzzle 10

F: Famine; O: Off; I: Infant; R: Road; T: Turban; A: Attila; E: Emigrés; B: Blue; P: Pachyderm; D: Dressing; N: Noraid; J: (The) Jones'; S: Seventeen; H: Habit; V: Vertigo; G: Gigi; M: Molehills; W: War; C: Chaps; L: Light.

Solution: Puzzle 11

M: Maximum; O: Oxford; K: Kenyatta; D: Danube; J: Jockey; P: Polychrome or polychromatic; H: Honour; W: Walls; F: Foil; B: Baseball; L: Local; S: Sturgeon; T: Tuesday; R: Regicides; C: Callaghan; E: Editor; A: Actors; V: Vixen; G: Grey; N: Neck.

Solution: Puzzle 12

C: Chicory; I: Ill; N: Nolan; O: Ostend; F: Fructose; K: Knickers; A: Alkali; P: Printing; D: Doh; W: Washington; B: Bat; G: Grace; H: Hydrogen; L: Loins; S: Storm; R: Raze; E: Eradicate; M: Maoris; T: Tusk; U: Underdone.

Solution: Puzzle 13

G: Giant; Y: Yoghourt; A: Adder; T: Tendril; W: Wheat; S: Sire; U: Unoccupied; B: Brackets; E: Ethiopia; N: Newspeak; C: Carbon; L: Land; P: Periwinkle; O: Oxon; H: Hercules; F: Forenoon; D: Dounreay; M: Maple; J: Johnson; R: Red.

Solution: Puzzle 14

C: Cardiff; E: Enzyme; H: Hardy; N: Nero; R: Robot; W: Wine; D: Drift; K: Knell; B: Beveridge; V: Van Dyke; F: Foot; T: Tanning; S: Sake; O: Obelisk; L: Log; G: Golden; P: Paul (St); M: Murdoch; J: Jet; A: Autobahn.

Solution: Puzzle 15

F: Flag; O: Observatory; I: Injection; R: Rubber; T: Tail; A: Annie; E: Eden; B: Blondin; P: Panacea; D: Dam; N: Noble (savage); J: Joss; S: Salmon; H: Hungary; V: Vagabond; G: Giotto; M: Monetarist; W: Wireless; C: Cenotaph; L: Leaf.

Solution: Puzzle 16

M: Matterhorn; O: Osmond; K: Kill; D: Dalyell; J: Jerusalem; P: Pommy; H: Henpecked; W: Wordsworth; F: Flutter; B: Bellows; L: Lamour; S: Saccharin; T: Troy; R: Rapid; C: Catch; E: Edward (Heath); A: Admirals; V: Vellum; G: Greece; N: Nesbit.

Solution: Puzzle 17

C: Candle; I: Immerse; N: Newmarket; O: Optimism; F: Frontispiece; K: Knick knack; A: Apostles; P: Pyjamas; D: Dogs; W: Wand; B: Batman; G: Guilder; H: Herriot; L: Loft; S: Salmon (note: Salmo Trutta is the same as Sea Trout); R: Reichstag; E: Equity; M: Max; T: Tupolev (The TU 144 pre-dated Concorde); U: Universal.

Solution: Puzzle 18

G: Ghost; Y: Yorkshire; A: Ant; T: Tarzan; W: Woodpecker; S: Sleeper; U: Union; B: Bandy; E: Exclusion; N: Nap; C: Church; L: Labrador; P: Perjury; O: Onomatopoeic; H: Henley; F: Flaxen; D: Diesel; M: Madeira; J: John; R: Raffia.

Solution: Puzzle 19

C: Caw; E: Ever; H: Hygiene; N: Neck; R: Romeo; W: Winchester; D: Dandy; K: Kodak; B: Batman; V: Vaudeville; F: Folk; T: Tanker; S: Solstice; O: Onions; L: Leicester; G: Gold; P: Passion; M: Mulberry; J: Jodhpurs; A: Alexander.

Solution: Puzzle 20

F: Fish; O: Oscar; I: Interrogation; R: Rhondda; T: Telescope; A: Authorised; E: Ensign; B: Bow; P: Pontoon; D: Decoy; N: New; J: Jenny; S: Spoonerisms; H: Hopscotch; V: Ventriloquist; G: Gazetteer; M: Money; W: Wattle; C: Century; L: Loaf.

Solution: Puzzle 21

M: Martin; O: Old; K: Kitten; D: Davits; J: Japan; P: Ptolemy; H: Hotpot; W: Wishbone; F: Flat; B: Bench; L: Lace; S: Spy; T: Tiara; R: Ransom; C: Camp; E: Eliot (George); A: Adriatic; V: Vertibrae; G: Grenada; N: Namby.

Solution: Puzzle 22

C: Canal; I: Iceland; N: Newfoundland; O: Oedipus; F: Fire; K: Kangaroo; A: Auden; P: Pawn; D: Dilate; W: Whisk; B: Bligh; G: Grumpy; H: Hummingbird; L: Loire; S: Silver; R: Raleigh; E: Ex-directory; M: Mantilla; T: Tepid; U: Uppers.

Solution: Puzzle 23

G: Germany; Y: Yew; A: Avocado; T: Thorn; W: Wren; S: Staple; U: Urchin; B: Bracken; E: Eel; N: Nail; C: Carrion; L: Love; P: Pinkie; O: O'Connor; H: Hockey; F: Forestry; D: Dark; M: Masquerade; J: Journalism; R: Rank.

Solution: Puzzle 24

C: Chess; E: Evening; H: Hyde; N: Noah; R: Requiem; W: Willow; D: Danger; K: Koala; B: Black; V: VAT; F: Family; T: Tamworth; S: Stake; O: O'Connell; L: Lieder; G: Glasgow; P: Pfennig; M: Mouse; J: Jersey; A: Ashes (The).

Solution: Puzzle 25

F: First; O: Orphan; I: Illuminate; R: Resurrection; T: Twelve; A: Architecture; E: Eight; B: Brain; P: Petain; D: Disraeli; N: Nore; J: Jaw; S: Socks; H: Horizontal; V: Vibrate; G: Gammon; M: Monolith; W: Weary; C: Ceefax; L: Leopold.

Solution: Puzzle 26

M: Manchester; O: O'Hara; K: Key; D: Disraeli; J: Jaundiced; P: Push; H: Haiti; W: Waterloo; F: Flail; B: Benjamin; L: Latex; S: Squash; T: Taiwan; R: Rear; C: Cayenne; E: Eighteen; A: Adelaide; V: Victory (83); G: Greene; N: Naseby.

Solution: Puzzle 27

C: Canada; I: Iberian; N: Nitric; O: Ostrich; F: Francis; K: Kookaburra; A: Asquith; P: Pocket; D: Doves; W: White; B: Blood; G: Grid; H: Hunting; L: Locomotive; S: Straight; R: Robot; E: Eyebrow; M: Mohicans; T: Tensing; U: Unleavened.

Solution: Puzzle 28

G: Gamble; Y: Young (Ones); A: Arson; T: Tintin (Hergé died in 1983); W: Woolwich; S: Sprat; U: Udder; B: Boots; E: Earmark; N: Nappy; C: Calorie; L: Lamb; P: Phrenology; O: One-armed; H: Hawks; F: Fungi; D: Dogger; M: Murder; J: Judgement; R: Referendum.

Solution: Puzzle 29

C: Château; E: Evans; H: Hybrid; N: Needlewoman; R: Rhubarb; W: Whit; D: Dresden; K: Knuckle; B: Blind; V: Velvet; F: Facile; T: Tamil; S: Steeplechase; O: Only; L: 'Lace'; G: Gnaw; P: Paralysis; M: Mortar; J: Junk; A: Australia.

Solution: Puzzle 30

F: Fairy; O: Olympic; I: Interval; R: Rigging; T: Type; A: Amputation; E: Egyptians; B: Boston; P: Pastry; D: Digestion; N: Numismatics (or -ism); J: Jung; S: Sputnik; H: Hope; V: Vaccination; G: Geese; M: Monument; W: Wagtail; C: Crocodiles; L: Loud.

Solution: Puzzle 31

M: Mankind; O: Octane; K: Kick; D: Duck; J: Jewish; P: Play; H: Hawks; W: Windmill; F: Fluent; B: Bahamas; L: Luftwaffe; S: Spain; T: Tweeter; R: Radicals; C: Canaries; E: Egypt; A: Antelope; V: Vincent; G: Golden; N: Nancy.

Solution: Puzzle 32

C: Cairn; I: Isben; N: Napoleon; O: Orange; F: Flag; K: Knotty; A: Afrikaans; P: Perpendicular; D: Doughboys; W: Winchester; B: Bank; G: Guitar; H: Hythe; L: Lion; S: Simple; R: Rasputin; E: Evacuees; M: Miser; T: Terylene; U: Universe.

Solution: Puzzle 33

G: Geneva; Y: Yale; A: Arctic; T: Thunder; W: Woden; S: Suez; U: Ultimatum; B: Boo; E: Exorbitant; N: Necklace; C: Colander; L: Lancaster; P: Pine; O: Occupational; H: Head; F: Fiver; D: Demote; M: Magnetic; J: Judy; R: Rainbow.

Solution: Puzzle 34

C: Chronological; E: Entrechat; H: Handwriting; N: Neptune; R: Reptilia; W: Whisper; D: Drivel; K: Kirk; B: Barter; V: Vermin; F: Florence; T: Tadpole; S: Spud; O: Obtuse; L: Lake; G: Gluttony; P: Pen; M: Moors; J: Juliet; A: Aqueduct.

Solution: Puzzle 35

F: Farrow; O: Olive; I: Intestine; R: Reveille; T: Triffids; A: Attlee; E: Ensign; B: Bounty; P: Philosophers; D: Dialect; N: Novel; J: Jerry; S: Satisfaction ('Can't Get No Satisfaction'); H: Horoscope; V: Viking; G: Galileo; M: Moon; W: Waffle; C: Croupier; L: Licorice.

Solution: Puzzle 36

M: Mars; O: Ostend; K: Keep; D: Didgerydoo; J: Jellyfish; P: Punt; H: Heiress; W: Wolf; F: Fur; B: Bishop; L: Liechtenstein; S: Sickle; T: Tyne; R: Ranch; C: Czechoslovakia; E: Eskimos; A: Aristotle; V: Venice (So-called because prisoners crossed it on their way to prison); G: Golf; N: Nana.

Solution: Puzzle 37

C: Cauliflower; I: Ibiza; N: Northumberland; O: Ordinary; F: Feather;
K: Kestrel; A: Albania; P: Persimmon; D: Dramatist; W: West; B: Blow;
G: Gunners; H: Hammer; L: Lions; S: Sea; R: Reap; E: Embassy;
M: Mahogany; T: Toilet; U: Understudy.

Solution: Puzzle 38

G: Gun; Y: Yen; A: Apennines; T: Thousand; W: Woburn; S: Stile;
U: Umpire; B: Box; E: Eros; N: Nanny; C: Cobalt; L: Laryngitis;
P: Photography; O: Obtain; H: Harrow; F: Fixed; D: Durham; M: Malaria;
J: Jugoslavia; R: Rabbits.

Solution: Puzzle 39

C: Chub; E: Ette; H: Hypnotised; N: Nettlerash; R: Roger; W: Whiskey;
D: Dates; K: Kipper; B: Block; V: Venetian; F: Fabians; T: Tactics;
S: Stockpot; O: Octane; L: Lasso; G: Glider; P: Permutation; M: Mother;
J: Jinx; A: Aluminium.

Solution: Puzzle 40

F: Feet; O: Oyster; I: Interview; R: Richelieu; T: Tarry; A: Asylum;
E: Eternity; B: Box; P: Passenger; D: Dispenser; N: Nomad; J: Jaguar;
S: Submarine; H: Harvest; V: Vatican; G: Gold; M: Mocha; W: Waltz;
C: Crab; L: Lot.

Solution: Puzzle 41

M: Margaret; O: Overture; K: Kilimanjaro; D: Dostoevsky; J: Jib;
P: Pulpit; H: Helen; W: Whinny; F: Foreign; B: Bell; L: Leningrad;
S: Sorbet; T: Two; R: Railing; C: Canute; E: Etching; A: Anthracite;
V: Violinists; G: Guards; N: Neapolitan.

Solution: Puzzle 42

C: Churn; I: Igloo; N: Nobby; O: Observatories; F: Fourteen; K: Kalahari;
A: Alibi; P: Petticoat; D: Doze; W: Wellington; B: Bucket; G: Gurkhas;
H: Harmonium; L: Linoleum; S: Second; R: Radish; E: Eyes; M: Man;
T: Tape; U: Upstairs.

Solution: Puzzle 43

G: Guatemala; Y: Yuletide; A: Achilles; T: Tip; W: Wife; S: Soul;
U: Upper; B: Boat; E: Era; N: Napoleon; C: Charollais; L: Lobster;
P: Phoenix; O: Offpeak; H: Handle; F: Feather; D: Dog; M: Mallory;
J: Julian; R: Richard III.

Solution: Puzzle 44

C: Chimaera (or Chimera); E: Euphoria; H: Hussein; N: New; R: Rock;
W: Whalebone; D: Diabetes; K: Koh-i-noor; B: Barber's; V: Venom;
F: Fairbanks; T: Teddy; S: Sustaining; O: Octave; L: Lace; G: Glasscloth;
P: Period or point; M: Moore; J: (Dr) Jekyll; A: Apples.

Solution: Puzzle 45

F: Fireworks; O: Obituary; I: Israel; R: Racket; T: Taster; A: Albert;
E: Eggs; B: Bullrush; P: Parkhurst; D: Dinosaurs; N: Nobel; J: Josephine;
S: Sack; H: Hops; V: Virgo; G: Gamma; M: Monkeys; W: Wedding;
C: Cancer; L: Lame.

Solution: Puzzle 46

M: Marmalade; O: Overhaul; K: Kid; D: Dickens; J: Jest; P: Prod;
H: Hindenburg; W: Wing; F: Finale; B: Beef; L: Law; S: Sea; T: Turin;
R: Razor; C: Chicory; E: Ear; A: Automobile; V: Viceroy; G: Gherkin;
N: Nephritic.

Solution: Puzzle 47

C: Cow; I: Icon; N: Napoleon; O: Ottoman; F: Forty; K: Kerosene;
A: Annie (Oakley in 'Get your gun'); P: Petrucchio; D: Dice; W: Watched;
B: Bananarama; G: Gradient; H: Holy; L: Lark; S: Shah; R: Rain(fall);
E: Eskimos; M: Mallard; T: Temple; U: Unction.

Solution: Puzzle 48

G: Golden; Y: Yarn; A: Albino; T: Thousand; W: Wine; S: Scapegoat;
U: Urn; B: Bluebird; E: Exchange; N: Nave; C: Captain; L: Little; P: Pink;
O: Opal; H: Hands; F: Forecourt; D: Dilettante; M: MacGregor (Sir Ian);
J: Junction; R: Ratty (because 'water rats' are really voles).

Solution: Puzzle 49

C: Copper; E: Envy; H: Hornet; N: Neutron; R: Roses; W: Wells (H.G.);
D: Drill; K: Koran; B: Boar; V: Varicose; F: Fancy; T: Toby;
S: Squeeze-box; O: Odd; L: Larvae; G: Giro; P: Piazza; M: Mortimer;
J: Jane; A: Alexander.

Solution: Puzzle 50

F: Fan; O: Offal; I: Intestate; R: Reading; T: Tavern; A: Archery;
E: Education; B: Bow; P: Paratroops; D: Discount; N: Note; J: Jackal;
S: Sauerkraut; H: Hail; V: Vegetable; G: Grace; M: Monster; W: Wag;
C: Cranberry; L: Landscape.

Solution: Puzzle 51

M: MacCarthy; O: Outcrop; K: Keats; D: Doge; J: Juliet; P: Prodigy;
H: Hosts; W: Wellington; F: Fairy; B: Beethoven; L: Luxembourg;
S: Sterling; T: Theology; R: Republics; C: Crocodile; E: Errand; A: Air;
V: Voltaire; G: Graham; N: Nose.

Solution: Puzzle 52

C: Charcoal; I: Identikit; N: Nana; O: Object; F: Filthy; K: Kale (kail);
A: Arctic; P: Peso; D: Dollar; W: Wrought; B: Bluebell; G: Gutenberg;
H: Harry; L: Lead; S: Sedgemoor (Note: 1685); R: Regatta; E: Earthquake;
M: Madonna; T: Thrush; U: Unanimous.

Solution: Puzzle 53

G: Gospels; Y: Yanks: A: Atmosphere; T: Thisbe; W: Windy; S: Sardines;
U: Ulterior; B: Bit; E: Evolution; N: National; C: Cap; L: Lemmings;
P: Pilot; O: Off-licence; H: Hapsburg; F: Falstaff; D: Dyes; M: Mongoose;
J: Joust; R: RADA.

Solution: Puzzle 54

C: Caretaker; E: Envelope; H: Horn; N: Nose; R: Roundabout; W: Weller;
D: Dugout; K: Kindle; B: Barchester; V: Veterinary; F: Faggot; T: Tom;
S: Sparticus; O: Ode; L: Ladder; G: Ginger; P: Pocahontas; M: Money;
J: Jordan; A: Aquarius.

Solution: Puzzle 55

F: Four; O: Oblong; I: Ink; R: Rabies; T: Truce; A: Artists; E: Eden;
B: Bournemouth; P: Papyrus; D: Demerara; N: Napkin; J: Jackdaw;
S: Salary; H: Haricot; V: Vegan; G: Game; M: Mother; W: Wicket;
C: Crystal; L: Llama.